ROCKED AND
RUPTURED

ROCKED AND RUPTURED

Geological Faults in New Zealand

Jefley J. Aitken

REED

in association with the Institute of Geological & Nuclear
Sciences Limited, Lower Hutt, New Zealand

Front cover photograph: Fissure in the water-saturated soft sediments of the Rangitaiki Plains associated with the Edgecumbe earthquake in 1987. This sadly domestic location has noticeable vertical and horizontal displacement on the plane of the Edgecumbe Fault.

Back cover photograph: The Alpine Fault exposed at Hokuri Creek north of Lake McKerrow in southern Westland. The deformed grey rocks at left are among New Zealand's oldest at more than 400-million-years old. The upright dark grey rock in the centre is the soft gooey pug of the fault plane, which is nearly vertical in this segment of the Alpine Fault, and the movement is all strike-slip. The brownish rocks at right are river and glacier gravels less than a million years old.

Published by Reed Books, a division of Reed Publishing (NZ) Ltd, 39 Rawene Rd, Birkenhead, Auckland. Associated companies, branches and representatives throughout the world.

ISBN 0 7900 0720 7
First published 1999

Printed in New Zealand

CONTENTS

FOREWORD

New Zealand's location, on the boundary between two of the earth's massive tectonic plates, is a double-edged sword.

The movement of these plates has twisted and contorted the earth to create a country of spectacular natural beauty. A country with mountains, lakes and fiords, wild rivers and geothermal wonders.

But this movement has also created a land where the threat of natural disasters is ever-present.

As a nation we have been at the forefront of world efforts to learn more about how the earth works and how to minimise the damage caused when the land beneath us buckles and deforms.

The Earthquake Commission has had a significant role to play in this process. In addition to providing insurance for homeowners so that they are able to recover quickly from the effects of natural disasters, the Commission also facilitates research and education into matters relevant to natural disaster damage.

While organisations such as EQC can take a lead in natural disaster damage mitigation, future success depends on all New Zealanders taking responsibility for their own lives and property. The first step is to ensure we all better understand the forces of nature and therefore the risks we face.

During the past 50 years, since the establishment of EQC's unique scheme, geological activity in New Zealand has been relatively benign. This has allowed funds to accumulate so that there is now a substantial sum available to help people recover from a major event.

However, the other side of the coin is that, with decreasing numbers of people who have experienced the effects of large earthquakes, it becomes more difficult to raise general awareness of the risk.

So we welcome *Rocked and Ruptured* as an excellent addition to New Zealand's seismological library. It is a book that will foster interest and understanding of the geological processes that have such a profound effect on our lives and thereby encourage us all to take the actions needed to limit their consequences.

David Middleton
General Manager, Earthquake Commission

ROCKED AND RUPTURED

Rock moves.
Different rocks move at different rates.
Rocks collide.
Pressure builds.
Rocks deform, until
something snaps.

The something snapping creates an earthquake. The earth quakes because rock has ruptured along paths of weakness, and the ruptured rocks jump to a new position. The pressure drops, but …

Rock keeps moving.
Different rocks keep moving at different rates.
Rocks keep colliding.
Pressure keeps building.
Rocks keep deforming, until
something snaps.

The something snapping creates an earthquake. Again. The earth quakes because rock has ruptured along paths of weakness, and the ruptured rocks jump to a new position. Again. The pressure drops, but …

Rock keeps right on moving.
Different rocks keep right on moving at different rates.
Rocks keep right on colliding.
Pressure keeps right on building.
Rocks keep right on deforming, until
something snaps.

The something snapping creates an earthquake. Yet again. The earth quakes because rock has ruptured along paths of weakness, and the ruptured rocks jump to another new position. Yet again. The pressure drops, but …

Them rocks, they just a-keep right on a-moving …
And, to cut a geologically eternal story short,
Them earthquakes keep right on a-happening.

Forewarned

This book explains the occurrence of New Zealand earthquakes and the processes that cause them, and illustrates their effects on the landscape. The study of earthquakes is called seismology, from the Greek *seismos*, meaning trembling earth. Seismologists have a background in geophysics, the discipline that uses physics to understand the invisible structures and processes far below the surface of the earth.

Paleoseismologists investigate the location, the size, and the timing of past earthquakes through fieldwork and a geologist's understanding of rocks and geological structures at the surface. They study earth deformation and displacements of geological faults where they rupture the earth's surface in order to find patterns of earthquake recurrence through time and space. The distribution of past earthquakes is the key to forecasting future earthquakes at a particular place and within a particular timeframe. Such knowledge is critical to planning safe communities and the recovery of nationally important structures and services such as roads, bridges, electricity and water.

Apart from the gurgling of volcanic materials under volcanic regions, all New Zealand's earthquakes are the result of its location across the boundary between the Pacific and Australian tectonic plates. This book begins with the theory of plate tectonics and finishes with earthquake prediction for beginners. Enjoy.

THE BIG PICTURE

Earthquakes are an ongoing effect of the continuous recycling of tectonic plates. The outer 100 km of the earth is divided into eight major plates and five significant smaller ones (figure 1). These giant slabs move across the surface of the planet, and are constantly being created at oceanic ridges and just as constantly destroyed at deep-sea trenches. Most of the planet's geological dramas, surface deformation and earthquakes are near boundaries between the plates.

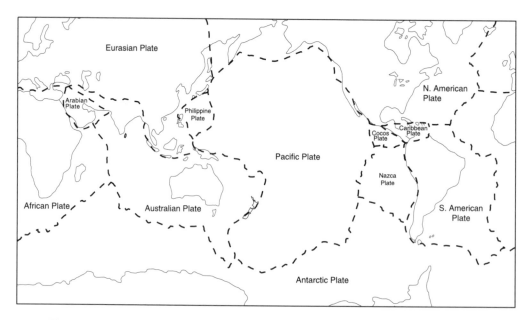

Figure 1 Major tectonic plates. Boundaries between plates are just lines on maps, but the stresses caused by moving plates affect vast areas of rock near the boundaries. The directly stressed interfaces between tectonic plates jigsaw around the world to depths of about 100 km, which is the average thickness of the plates.

A line on a map that represents a 5-km stretch of boundary between two tectonic plates indicates 500 square kilometres of directly stressed rock interface (5 km long by 100 km deep). And, of course, the stress affects rocks tens of kilometres back into the plates from the boundary. Accordingly, a map line depicting 5 km of boundary may indicate 200,000 cubic kilometres of stressed and deforming rock below the surface. The cool and brittle upper parts of these huge three-dimensional areas are veritable homelands for earthquakes because, like the springs of clockwork toys, rock deformation has its limits. When the deformation becomes greater than the strength of the rocks and the friction that holds them together, the stress is released in an earth-quaking rupture.

A world map of earthquakes mimics the map of tectonic plates to an astonishing degree (figure 2). Some earthquake zones are narrow, some are hundreds of kilometres wide. Zones that run through oceans generally host small earthquakes, while those around the edges can have huge quakes. Nearly three-quarters of the planet's big quakes occur around the edge of the Pacific Ocean, where oceanic tectonic plates dive along deep-sea trenches and plunge beneath their more buoyant continental neighbours.

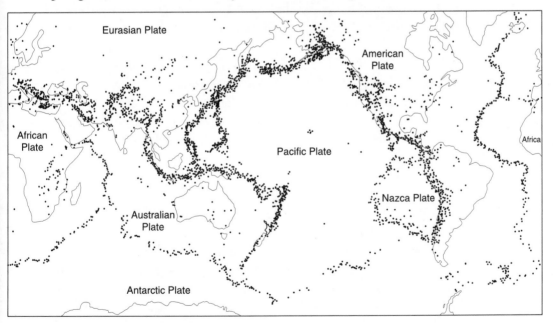

Figure 2 A decade's worth of earthquakes with magnitudes greater than 4.5 show the close relationship between earthquakes and tectonic plate boundaries. Earthquakes occasionally happen within tectonic plates, that is, far from their boundaries, but usually these occur with rather less energy, and rather less often. The numerous earthquakes that are associated with the creation of plate material at oceanic ridges seldom cause damage to coastal communities.

The movement of plates down deep-sea trenches is called subduction. Although most of the plate boundaries around the Pacific Ocean involve subduction, there are also sections, such as in California and New Zealand's South Island, where the boundary cuts through a continental mass of buoyant rock.

New Zealand is by no means alone in having to include earthquakes in its plans for the future. The largest earthquake recorded by modern instruments (at magnitude 9.5) occurred in Chile, on the opposite side of the Pacific, in 1960. It resulted from the Nazca Plate subducting under the South American Plate along a 1000-km stretch of coast, in one 30-metre thrust. It also created an enormous tsunami that drowned 61 people in distant Hawaii.

A tsunami is a small, but fast, ocean wave caused by a submarine earthquake, landslide, or volcanic eruption. It becomes a large and slow coastal wave as the ocean's depth decreases. Tsunami can be major killers hundreds and thousands of kilometres from their source. In the northeast Pacific, the magnitude 9.3 Alaskan earthquake in 1964 created a 12-metre-high tsunami and caused uplift or downdrop over 200,000 square kilometres as the Pacific Plate lurched under the North American Plate.

Japan, in the northwest Pacific, has an entire catalogue of catastrophic earthquakes because of the subduction of the Pacific Plate beneath the Eurasian Plate. The largest recorded this century was the magnitude 7.9 Kanto earthquake in 1923. It almost completely destroyed Tokyo and Yokohama, and was responsible for about 100,000 deaths.

There is no doubt that New Zealand, in the southwest Pacific, has had comparably enormous earthquakes. Moreover, there is every reason to assume that the ongoing convergence of the Pacific and Australian plates will continue to generate these in the future. New Zealand's current level of earthquake activity is not as high as in Japan, but is similar to that of California.

Hazards created by earthquakes range from nuisance to fatal, but it is not actually the earthquakes that kill. Most deaths occur when buildings and other 'cultural' structures collapse from the shaking. The 'natural' killers are the landslides and tsunami that sometimes accompany earthquakes, not the quakes themselves. Apart from collapsed buildings, interrupted supplies of water, electricity and gas, and broken sewage and communication systems, uncontrolled fires and blocked roads and bridges can tragically disrupt lives and communities. These calamities are, however, peculiarly human and, as such, their consequences can be minimised by research and organisation.

Seismologists work with other geoscientists to build a picture of earthquake processes and patterns so that the hazards in different areas can be estimated. By understanding the distribution, frequency and severity of earthquakes in a particular region, planners, architects and engineers can lessen the disruption. They 'zone' around hazardous areas, develop construction codes appropriate to the hazard levels, and create safer buildings and structures.

Similarly, with scientific information on the geohazards in their areas, local and regional authorities can develop procedures to cope with a crisis. The best strategies for surviving earthquakes with minimised disruption, however, come from educated communities where individuals can reach sensible decisions within their own homes, contribute to informed public debate, and follow Civil Defence guidelines and instructions.

It is, perhaps, unfortunate that there has been only one onshore earthquake in New Zealand greater than magnitude 7 in the last 45 years — the one in the sparsely populated Inangahua area in 1968. Consequently, there are relatively few people with firsthand experience of what to do and what not to do during an earthquake, and with personal plans for 'the next time'. Such a long period of earthquake quietness is not particularly unusual because — and here comes the bad news — large earthquakes sometimes come in clusters. Between 1929 and 1934 there were five onshore earthquakes greater than magnitude 7.

New Zealanders should consult the last entries in the Yellow Pages of their telephone directories. Civil Defence information is always important, and one dreadful day it may be crucial.

PLATES AND QUAKES

Consequences of the movements of tectonic plates include earthquakes, volcanoes, geothermal activity, mountain chains, tsunami, and landslides. These consequences are particularly influential, unavoidable, and irreducible near the boundaries between plates — such as the one that runs through the New Zealand region (plates 1–5). California's geological faults, Washington's volcanoes, Japan's earthquakes, the Philippines' volcanoes, Peru's mountain chains, and Chile's geothermal areas all have counterparts in New Zealand. This makes it worthwhile for New Zealanders to understand the structure and processes of tectonic plates, and the way that their movement causes rock to rupture and the earth to quake.

All this movement occurs because the earth has different concentric layers with different chemical ingredients and physical characteristics. The rigid 100-km-thick tectonic plates (from the Greek *tekton* for builder, and the same 'tect' as in architecture) are the ultimate recycling triumph. They are mainly created at volcanic ridges in oceans where molten rock wells up through cracks thousands of kilometres long. This molten rock solidifies and the two sides of the crack move horizontally in opposite directions as new tectonic plate material. Plates are commonly destroyed at deep-sea trenches near the edges of oceans by the subduction process; they sink along these trenches and are recycled back into the molten rock of the earth's interior.

The driving force behind the movement of plates is heat. The outer ten percent of the planet follows patterns similar to those seen on a kitchen stove any day of the week — hot material rises and expands while cold material sinks and contracts. Other friendly comparisons with the kitchen include the relatively rigid and dense nature of cold material ('Eeks! — It's frozen solid') compared with the more fluid tendencies of hot material.

Differences in temperature and density create movement. Differences between one place and another within a material promote directed movement

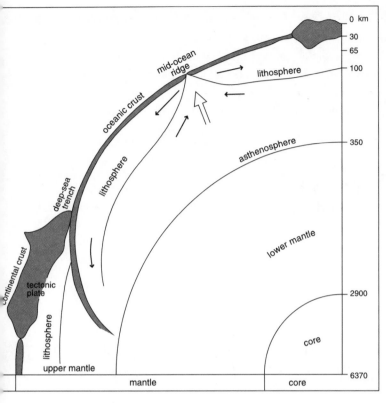

Figure 3 The earth's concentric layers. The 6000°C core is mainly iron and nickel. The mantle has subdivisions, including a crust, with chemical, physical, and behavioural differences.

Chemically speaking, if the planet were a plum, the core would be the stone, the mantle the fruit, and the crust the skin.

Physically based mantle subdivisions are a stiff and solid lower layer, a hot, mobile middle layer called the asthenosphere, and a rigid and brittle outer layer called the lithosphere. The lower mantle and the asthenosphere range from 4000°C to 1400°C near the surface. It is the lithosphere and its crust that form tectonic plates. (Not to scale.)

away from cool regions and towards warm regions. Scientists call this temperature-directed movement 'convection'. Some planetary heat is created by the radioactive decay of chemical elements such as uranium, but the roughly 6000°C temperatures in the core mainly trigger thermal convection currents within the earth. Convection cells drive the creation of tectonic plates, their movement across the surface, and their eventual destruction. In fact, the plates are the cold parts of the thermal convection cells of the planet (figure 3).

About 100 km down from the earth's surface, the temperature approaches 1400°C and some rocks are partially molten. This is the boundary zone between tectonic plates (remember, they comprise the lithosphere and its crust) and the underlying asthenosphere. The asthenosphere deforms and flows, and is sufficiently hot, soft, and mobile to allow the plates to move about on it. Because of this pliability, the asthenosphere does not store energy in a way that can be abruptly released by a rupture within rocks that creates earthquakes.

The temperature of rocks, therefore, restricts their earthquake potential. Although tectonic plates move as rigid slabs of lithosphere and crust, only the top 15 to 20 km are generally cool and brittle enough to store energy that can be abruptly released in earthquakes. The exception is when cool crust is carried down in subduction zones. Temperatures within the outer 20 km increase from the cool surface downwards, at an average rate of 30°C for every kilometre of depth. At temperatures greater than about 600°C, some types of rock can partly accommodate tectonic stress. They can 'go with the flow' and transfer energy in a ductile manner, rather than store it in finite deformation patterns until they snap and fracture as a brittle material.

See the science for yourself

Heating white honey and freezing golden honey are good ways to see physical changes that occur because of changes in temperature. Almost any honey on hot toast develops an alarming mobility ... beware. Similarly, it is very difficult to move hokey-pokey bits around in frozen icecream, but as the icecream becomes warmer it becomes easier to poke the hokey-pokey around.

Subduction

Subducting plates create deep earthquakes. Different plates move at different speeds and the speeds can vary through time. These variations depend on the length and the proportion of the boundary that subducts. The speed of a plate also varies along different segments of its boundary and this has a strong influence on the distribution and frequency of earthquakes. Bending down a trench creates both extension and compression stresses, and the faster a plate travels through the bending point, the greater the frequency of earthquakes.

A quickly subducting segment of plate stays colder, more rigid, and more brittle at greater depths, and can therefore host deeper earthquakes — down to nearly 700 km. A more slowly subducting part, however, has time to be influenced by its red-hot environment. A slower plate (or segment of plate) becomes pliable and loses its ability to snap and rupture before it reaches great depths.

This speed–temperature relationship can be demonstrated by plunging an ice-cube into a hot bath — the depth to which the ice-cube remains rigid and brittle depends on the speed of immersion. The fastest plates are those with the longest subduction boundaries, such as the Pacific and Nazca plates. The slowest plates have a negligible proportion of subduction boundary, for example, the Eurasian and Antarctic plates. The average speed for plate movement is about 45 km every million years, which is roughly the growth rate of your fingernails, 45 mm per year or, apparently, the length that human hair grows over a lifetime.

Whether a plate will subduct or remain buoyant in the collision between two plates depends largely on the type and the amount of crust on the plate. Tectonic plates created at oceanic ridges are made of hot, dense materials and dense stuff sinks as it cools. These oceanic plates are relatively rich in magnesium, iron and calcium that combine to make a dense basalt crust on a lithosphere of coarse-grained rocks that are mostly composed of the same dense materials.

Continental crust, on the other hand, develops through a never-ending, varied and complicated recycling programme that results in unsinkable landmasses. This recycling programme is a very, very long and repetitive story that involves such surface processes as erosion, weathering, and volcanic activity, as well as geological cycles such as burial, uplift, and metamorphism. In a nutshell, continents are the scum of the earth ... Lightweight minerals that are rich in silicon, potassium and sodium dominate the enormous variety of rocks in continental crust, and there is a considerable chemical difference between this crust and its underlying lithosphere.

Oceanic crust is much thinner as well as much denser than continental crust. Oceanic crust averages 5 to 6 km and, although less dense than its underlying lithosphere, it is seldom a long-term hindrance to subduction processes. But the crustal portion of continental plates is quite different. Continental crust mostly ranges from 30 to 60 km thick (out of about 100 km for the whole plate), and this large proportion of buoyant crust keeps continental plates afloat. When continental plates run into another plate they cannot subduct because of this buoyancy — which is why landmasses near a subduction boundary are part of the overriding plate.

Variation in the thickness of continental crust is mainly due to tectonic recycling, and sequences of deformation caused by tectonic stress. A certain amount of stress can be accommodated by the rocks being stretched or squashed out of shape — the geotechnical term for such a change of shape is 'strain', but 'deformation' is quite acceptable.

Where stress compresses rocks and squeezes them together, the crust is thicker. Where the stress is extensional and rocks are pulled apart because their plates are bending, the crust stretches and becomes thinner. Shear stress is a component of stress that causes sliding along a plane. Most forces are at oblique angles to zones of weakness, and they nearly always produce some lateral shearing movement when rocks rupture.

The amount of crust on different parts of a plate can dramatically influence collision behaviour in the short-term — within hundreds of years geologically speaking. Some parts of an oceanic plate have thicker than average crust, which makes them less dense and more difficult to subduct.

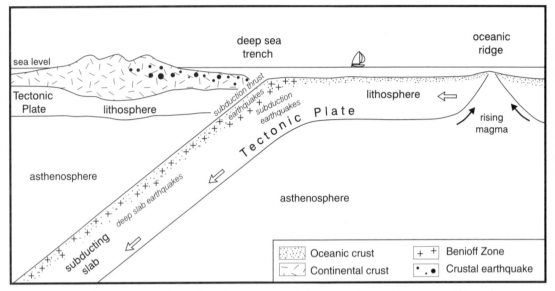

Figure 4 A tectonic boundary between a subducting plate and an overriding plate topped with continental crust. Benioff Zone earthquakes are marked by crosses. The subducting plate retains its cool even when its neighbourhood has turned red hot and, depending on its speed, can generate earthquakes down to nearly 700 km. Subduction, subduction-thrust, deep-slab, and crustal earthquakes are triggered by different processes in different areas.

Such areas may create large 'subduction-thrust' earthquakes. It has been estimated that these areas account for nearly 90 percent of the total seismic energy released during earthquakes in the last 90 years. Subduction often proceeds in lurches where thicker-crusted and hard-to-subduct segments lock up against the overlying plate. This locking is due to friction, in the same way that too much force on the brake pedal can lock the wheels of a car. Locally thick areas of continental crust overlying a subduction zone can also cause segments of the plate boundary to lock up and rupture in subduction-thrust earthquakes.

This friction means that tectonic plates seldom bend underneath, or move past, each other in a smooth well-oiled sort of progression. The movement can be graunching and grinding, tearing and shearing. Subduction zones and the continental crust above a subducting plate have such contrasting patterns of earthquakes that the subduction region has earned its own seismic label: the Benioff Zone.

American seismologist Hugo Benioff confirmed that shallow earthquakes are very common within oceanic plates where they start to bend and sink close to trenches. The change from horizontal travel across the sea floor to a dive along a deep-sea trench extends and stretches the material in the upper part of the plate, and compresses and squashes material along the bottom of the plate. Added to these earthquake-inducing stresses are twist, tear, and rip behaviours caused by different sections of the plate having different thicknesses of crust and subducting at different speeds.

Benioff found that earthquakes formed a pattern of increasing depth sloping under the overriding plate at about 45°. New Zealand has a well-developed Benioff Zone of earthquakes reaching depths of 300 km. As the subducting slab is pulled downwards it is stretched out, as part of the convection cycle, and extensional stresses cause earthquakes and ruptures within it. Quakes have been recorded from nearly 700-km depths, which indicates that some segments of the subducting plate remain sufficiently brittle to host earthquakes at those depths. Such 'deep-slab' earthquakes are felt on the surface (figure 4).

The graunching and grinding aspects of tectonic movement cause other types of earthquakes. A section of plate boundary can grind to a halt so that the plate surfaces stay locked together for hundreds of years. However, tectonic forces do not stop just because the going gets tough, and when the lock breaks, earthquakes may occur in two separate areas. As mentioned above, the locked interface between the plates may rupture and the subducting slab may abruptly lurch downwards, creating a huge subduction-thrust earthquake. The enormous 1960 Chile and 1964 Alaska earthquakes were of this subduction-thrust type.

The second area directly affected by a locked-together section of plate boundary is the overlying crust. Large and shallow 'crustal' earthquakes occur within the overlying continental crust as it deforms more and more because the energy for movement is dammed up behind the locked zone. If crustal rock ruptures right up to the surface, the results of this deformation are visible as the top edge of a geological fault, but most earthquakes are too small to do this.

Lines of active volcanoes commonly develop in the crust overlying a subduction zone. It is estimated that 37,000 km of volcanic chains lie parallel to subduction zones. These are called volcanic arcs, or (volcanic) island arcs. The Mariana Islands and the Tonga–Kermadec chain of islands both developed in crust parallel to a deep-sea trench and they are typical island arcs. The New Zealand chain of active volcanoes from White Island southward to Ruapehu, is an extension of the Tonga–Kermadec chain, but the continental landmass of the New Zealand region complicates and varies the process.

Side by side

Collisions between converging tectonic plates are not always solved by subduction. Where sections of two converging plates both have some continental
crust on their mutual boundary, subduction is impossible and a different sort
of process is activated to cope with the relentless tectonic stresses.

In some areas the tectonic action transforms from a downward subduction
movement into a lateral movement along a truly gigantic geological fault. This
enormous geological fault serves as a neutral plate boundary where, theoretically, plates are neither created nor destroyed. In reality, however, there is
often some destruction due to oblique stresses, and the sideways movement is
punctuated by shallow earthquakes of the very large and damaging variety.

So … sections of converging plates that are both edged with continental
crust can grind past each other sideways. This may cause one or both edges to
slowly buckle and crumple into long mountain ranges that parallel the fault.
This type of lateral-movement plate boundary is called a transform-fault
boundary. Such boundaries may not only link separated subduction zones
where sections of plates are unable to subduct, but they also link separated
sections of creative boundary at oceanic ridges, and creative and destructive
boundaries where these occur.

Transform-fault boundaries continue until tectonic conditions, such as the
development of a new convection cell, or the type or amount of crust on one of
the plates, change. The tectonic process then transforms from neutral to creative or destructive.

California's infamous San Andreas Fault is part of the boundary between
the Pacific and North American plates where the plates move sideways relative to one another. Residents of Los Angeles and San Francisco are becoming
more neighbourly by several centimetres each year. Closer to home, the South
Island's Alpine Fault separates bits of continental crust on the edges of both
the Australian and the Pacific plates (figure 5, plates 1 to 5). The trace of the
Alpine Fault is the visible result of the oblique convergence of the two plates,
and the stress is resolved by the uplift of the Southern Alps as well as the
plates moving sideways past each other.

LIFE ON THE EDGE

Earthquakes that rock and rupture New Zealand's countryside are a natural consequence of a life astride the edges of two tectonic plates. The boundary between the Pacific Plate and the Australian Plate splits the country, and the push-and-shove relationship between these two giant slabs of the earth's crust has rocked and ruptured New Zealand for about 25 million years. Earlier earthquakes were prompted by other tectonic systems.

The drama of the New Zealand situation develops because the Pacific and Australian plates are moving towards each other. The collision between two plates is rarely straightforward, but if prizes were offered for tectonic turmoil, New Zealand would be in with a big chance. The Pacific and Australian plates converge at a variety of angles and speeds, and the collision is resolved in three different ways; east-to-west subduction, west-to-east subduction, and by grinding past each other sideways.

The Pacific Plate does the subducting north of Kaikoura, and the Australian Plate does the subducting south of Milford Sound. Between the Milford and Kaikoura areas the downward subduction movements are transformed into sideways movement along the Alpine Fault. Added to all this commotion are oblique stresses that link and combine with subduction and lateral shearing movements. New Zealand is well and truly caught in the crunch.

The North Island has the entire register of tectonic symptoms that can be expected from sitting over a subducting plate; active faults, earthquakes, volcanoes and geothermal areas are the most obvious. Southwards to about Kaikoura, the Pacific Plate is edged with an unusually thick layer of oceanic crust. It is pulled down the Hikurangi Trough as the cold part of a convection cell, and subducted under the North Island at 40 to 60 mm per year. The pattern of earthquakes under the North Island indicates that the Hikurangi Trough is a very active and effective subduction gateway, even though it is less than half the depth of its northern extension, the Tonga–Kermadec Trench. Subduction rates decrease from an average 60 mm per year in the north to 30 mm per year in the south (figure 5).

The North Island embraces the entire spectrum of earthquake varieties. The quakes are mainly shallow in the east and originate at progressively greater depths towards the west, so subduction earthquakes and deep-slab earthquakes account for much of the seismic excitement. Shallow crustal earthquakes on active geological faults are typical results of deformation in the brittle crust above a subduction zone. Although historic records are too short to show a pattern, the abrupt unlocking of sections of boundary interface in subduction-thrust earthquakes is expected to produce very large quakes. To cap it all off, the central North Island is prone to volcanic earthquakes as molten rocks and gases rearrange themselves and fracture rock underneath and inside volcanoes.

The possibility of a textbook subduction zone east of the New Zealand area was scuppered about 30 million years ago. At that time, convection currents from within the planet started splitting the prehistoric New Zealand continental mass into two, so that it was no longer a coherent block of continental crust on just one tectonic plate. By 10 million years ago, the south and east of the South Island had become a blob of continental crust attached to the edge of the Pacific Plate. It was geologically separated from the rest of the country, which remained a continental outpost on the edge of the Australian Plate (figure 5).

With both sides of the divided South Island made of buoyant continental rock, subduction to relieve the tectonic stress was not an option. Neither side could sink, but the plates kept (and still keep) moving together. Something had to give. The course of least resistance proved to be a sideways shearing movement along an enormous geological fault accompanied, no doubt, by truly enormous earthquakes. This was the beginning of the Alpine Fault, which became a new segment of plate boundary. But the direction of the main stress is oblique to the zone of weakness, and the Southern Alps are a vertical deformity resulting from stress that is not transformed into sideways movement. They have been rapidly uplifted and exposed over the last 5 million years.

The Alpine Fault is one of the world's most spectacular transform boundaries. Its onshore section runs from Milford Sound to Blenheim. Geoscientists estimate that there has been about 470 km of lateral movement, 80 km of convergent movement, and 20 km of uplift across this segment of plate boundary. At no time, however, could mountaineers have had a 20-km high view, because rates of uplift are nearly equalled by those of erosion. Erosion takes the tops off the Southern Alps almost as fast as they are created. It is estimated that the rocks currently at the top of Mt Cook (plate 60) were below today's sea level not much more than a million years ago, and the present-day uplift and erosion rates are 8 to 10 mm per year.

About 10 million years ago the rocks of eastern Nelson on the Australian Plate and western Otago on the Pacific Plate were adjacent to each other (plates 1 and 2). Since then, lateral movement along the Alpine Fault has separated these former neighbours. The speed of the Pacific Plate relative to the Australian Plate along this fault has most recently averaged 37 mm per year and, although the rates have clearly changed with time, Christchurch and the entrance to Milford Sound will probably reach the same latitude within the next 10 million years.

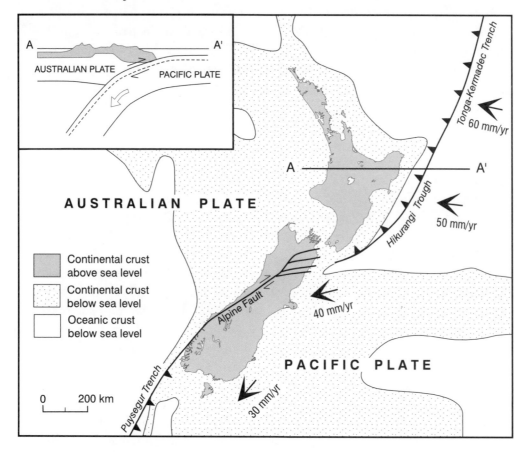

Figure 5 Canterbury, Otago and Southland are on the Pacific Plate. The North Island, Nelson and Westland are on the Australian Plate. The onshore boundary is represented by the Canterbury and Marlborough faults, and the massive Alpine Fault. The offshore subduction boundaries are the Tonga–Kermadec Trench and the Hikurangi Trough in the northeast, and the Puysegur Trench in the southwest. The arrows and numbers are the direction and average speed of the Pacific Plate relative to the Australian Plate.

While this seems more than enough tectonic torture for one small country, New Zealand's trauma does not end with oblique stresses along the transform-fault boundary. The Alpine Fault runs out to sea and smacks into oceanic crust just west of Milford Sound. Fiordland to the south is at the very edge of the Pacific Plate's blob of continental crust, and it butts against oceanic crust on the edge of the Australian Plate — the exact reverse of the North Island situation.

Consequently, the sideways movement along the Alpine Fault abruptly transforms into predominantly downward movement because the dense Australian oceanic crust can subduct under an obstacle such as a buoyant lump of New Zealand, even though it is only a small continental-rock outpost at the edge of a large oceanic plate. In this region, the Australian Plate subducts along the Puysegur Trench and under the Pacific Plate. This west-to-east subduction zone has not yet produced onshore volcanism or a geothermal area like that of the central North Island. The volcanic Solander Island in western Foveaux Strait is less than 2 million years old, but this volcano is considered extinct, and its relationship to the subduction zone is somewhat obscure. The pattern of earthquakes in Fiordland, however, is a compressed mirror image of that under the North Island. In Fiordland, the distribution pattern of earthquakes grades from shallow in the west to deep in the east.

The largest earthquake in the last 30 years is associated with this part of the plate boundary, and occurred about 800 km southwest of New Zealand. The magnitude 8.2 Macquarie Ridge earthquake in 1989 was only 10 km deep and involved sideways movement along the fault plane. It would have been devastating if it had occurred near a city but fortunately the nearest neighbours (all six of them) were scientists some 250 km away on Macquarie Island.

Another type of deformation that is common in New Zealand is warping — the bending of the earth's surface without a fault rupture, although a major fault is often not too far away. What were once flat, nearly horizontal surfaces, such as river terraces, are now warped, sometimes sloping up (instead of down) a valley. In some places, this deformation is accomplished by slippage between layers of sedimentary rock. Warping has been accompanied by some earthquakes, but little is known about whether it could occur as a consequence of long-continued tectonic stress without creating earthquakes.

Sticky-fingered and edible experiments

The sticky-fingered approach to understanding tectonic stress, rock deformation, earth-quaking ruptures, and the relationship between pressure, heat and rupture, involves chocolate bars of the gooey-interiored variety such as Moro, Mars, Pinky and Buzz Bars.

Compression stress and crustal thickening

Put the chocolate bar flat on the table with the palms of your hands against each end, and slowly squeeze your hands together. Depending on the temperature, the bar will deform by shortening and bulging out in the middle before the chocolate ruptures. Soft pliable matter deforms rather than ruptures, and the warmer it is the more it deforms. The rupturing of the brittle chocolate can be related to earthquakes and geological faults in the upper crust, while the deforming of the gooey caramel stuff is akin to the flowing behaviour of deeper, hotter rocks.

Extension stress and crustal thinning

Firmly hold each end of the chocolate bar and slowly pull your hands apart (soft and sticky bars work best; beware of the mess). The chocolate will crack apart and the bar will deform by lengthening, and thinning in the middle. A similar thinning effect can be mimicked by holding the middle of the bar between your thumb and third finger and squeezing. The resulting deformation shows local thinning (the thumb and finger dents), but there is no change in length. The material that was stressed out of its original position has moved laterally and created thickened areas adjacent to the directly stressed areas. Evidence for this redistribution of deforming stresses is not restricted to chocolate bars. Tectonic stresses never stop, they just change from one place to another, and from one time to the next, so that all rocks are constantly deforming to some extent.

Shear stress

This is not a post-traumatic disorder in sheep, but a casual reference to the tectonic force that produces lateral displacement of rocks along a rupture. Shear stress involves two parallel forces that aim in opposite directions. In a shear movement, formerly aligned points on the two sides of a rupture plane will move sideways relative to each other. I have not been able to reproduce shear stress and its consequent rupture with chocolate bars — but it was good fun trying!

Subduction trauma

To appreciate the various stresses acting on a subducting plate, take another chocolate bar and put it flat on a table, with about half of it hanging over the edge. Then, very slowly, press the overhanging edge downwards. Extension stress will crack the chocolate on the upper surface and the upper levels of caramel will deform by thinning. On the bottom surface, the chocolate ruptures because of compressive stress and the caramel crumples and locally thickens.

When you have demonstrated these stresses and deformities to your satisfaction, please feel free to eat the evidence.

THE FINAL STRAW

Rocks are stressed to different extents and in different directions, and they deform and rupture according to their strength and the local temperature. An earthquake occurs when tectonic stress builds up so much that a block of rock, deformed beyond its strength, suddenly cracks. It ruptures along a zone of weakness and lurches to a new position, releasing stored energy. This sudden lurch sets off the waves (the stored energy) that are felt at the surface as an earthquake.

Although the rupturing movement of one block against another can extend for hundreds of kilometres (for example, one side of a fault might move 3 metres northwards relative to the other throughout a 150-km stretch of countryside), the mechanical failure of the rock mass has to start somewhere. There is always a point where the rupture begins and, therefore, where the earthquake originates. This point is the 'focus' of an earthquake, and the point on the ground surface directly above the focus is the 'epicentre'. Earthquake maps plot epicentres and accordingly show the places directly above the places where earth-quaking ruptures have begun. Epicentres have been determined by computer since 1964 in New Zealand, and the advances in clever measuring tools and refinements in geophysical models mean that epicentres are now very accurately plotted.

The zone of weakness along which rock ruptures and creates an earthquake is rather emotionally termed a geological 'fault'. These faults always have rocks on one side of the rupture plane displaced relative to rocks on the other. Cracks in rock without displacement are called joints, not faults. The abrupt movement to a condition of little or no deformation is called elastic rebound (figure 6).

When the rocks on either side of a fault plane move relative to each other, the energy that deformed the rock is abruptly released. Like a clockwork toy that is wound tighter and tighter, the more that rocks are deformed, the more

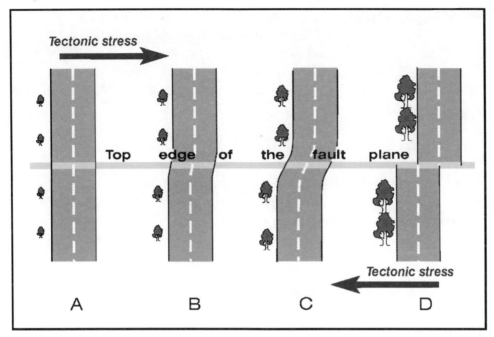

Figure 6 Time-lapse sketches of a road crossing the top edge of a fault to show deformation and elastic rebound. Relatively speaking, tectonic stresses push rock in the top half towards the right, and the bottom part towards the left.
A) The new road follows its planned straight path.
B) Decades later, the road develops a kink in response to the opposing tectonic forces.
C) Deformation continues to increase around the geological fault as decades pass.
D) Rocks rupture along the fault and elastically rebound to a position of less deformation.

energy they store. The amount of stored energy influences the size of the rupture — its length and depth. Moreover, the areal extent of the rupture, as well as the amount of displacement, influences the strength and frequency of vibrations that radiate outwards creating an earthquake.

The crust's reaction to these seismic waves depends mainly on local rock types, regional geological structure, the water table, and topography. In hard, compacted rocks, no significant amplification occurs, but in unconsolidated sediments and soft rocks the vibrations can be greatly amplified. Such unconsolidated materials may slump, flow or settle, especially where hills and slopes are steep. The loss of bearing strength that damages buildings and structures such as bridges can happen without visible changes on the surface.

After the disastrous 1906 Californian earthquake, seismologist Harry Reid examined the deformation and ruptures in areas along the San Andreas Fault, and he proposed an elastic-rebound mechanism to explain the earthquake and its surface effects (figure 6). (Earthquakes can be considered good medicine that restores a rock body to health after a long period of deformation.)

Although Reid's theory of elastic rebound has been somewhat refined and modified, modern research and seismological equipment have not necessitated a new theory to explain the many years of observations since Reid advanced his idea of elastic rebound.

Waves that quake the earth

Waves within a solid body are more complicated than waves made by throwing a stone into a pond. The shock waves that vibrate the earth are called seismic waves, and they come in three main varieties. Each type of wave travels at a different speed, creates a different type of vibration, and causes a different effect at ground level (figure 7). Complicating the picture even further is the tendency of seismic waves to vibrate at different strengths in different directions depending on their depth, the regional geology, and local rocks and soils.

The first wave to arrive at your place after an earth-quaking rupture travels like a sound wave, and it is sometimes heard rather than felt. The next is a shaking wave and it usually causes the main damage. These primary (P) and secondary (S) waves may be thought of as P-push and S-shake waves. They travel outwards in all directions from the earthquake source, often penetrating deep into the innards of the earth and surfacing on the far side of the planet. S-waves, however, cannot travel through water or liquid rock.

Because the speed of P-waves is about half as great again as that of S-waves, a single earthquake often feels like two quakes in places far from the focus. The time lag between lightning and thunder is similarly caused by the different speeds of light and sound waves — the greater the gap, the farther away the storm. When the focus of a quake is close to the earth's surface, surface waves may also be set up. These travel outward relatively slowly and horizontally, more like waves in the sea than P- or S-waves. The destruction as a result of the ground movement caused by surface waves can be greater than that caused by P- and S-waves, and it reaches its maximum after the other waves have passed.

Damage from ground shaking typically relates to the magnitude, or size, of the earthquake. The greater the magnitude, the longer the shaking and the greater the damage. The damage lessens with distance from the focus because the earth-shaking energy is dispersed and attenuated in the crust of the earth. Distance also applies in a vertical direction — damage from a particular-sized quake focused at 300-km depths is much less than the same-sized quake radiating from a focus 3 km deep.

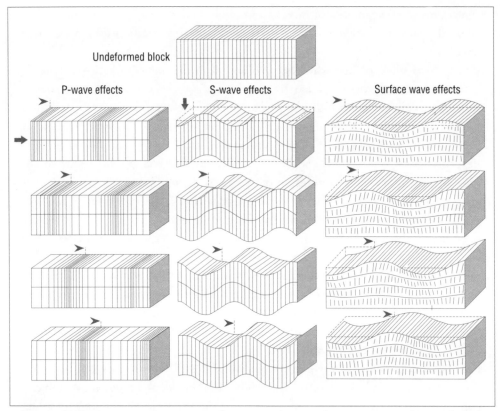

Figure 7 P-waves travel as zones of compression — they squeeze and stretch rock that they travel through. S-waves vibrate material up and down, as sketched in this diagram, or sideways. In addition, there are several types of surface wave, but they only travel across the surface, often with a circular motion like an ocean wave.

Generally, not all the stress that deforms rocks is released during an earthquake. Aftershocks may continue for weeks to years after a major quake, depending on its size, but they usually decrease in number as time goes by. Aftershocks seem to have several causes, and they are probably interrelated.

First, the movement along the fault that created the first quake might have redistributed the tectonic stresses in such a way that an adjacent area receives tens or hundreds of years' worth of deformation in one hit. This hurries a second area towards its breaking point, and its rupture, in turn, may affect another neighbouring area.

Another factor that may explain some aftershocks is the roughness of the fault surface. Just as faults are not straight surfaces — look at the wobbly traces in the photographs — they are also not smooth. Consequently, not all the movement of rocks may occur during the initial rupture. It is considered that quite small segments of fault might stick, and the rock blocks may adjust several times in a stick-and-slip pattern. Each slip could produce an aftershock.

A third view of aftershocks involves diminishing returns. Most of the deformation and most of its earth-quaking energy-release occurs at particular rates. It seems to take hundreds of years for the deforming energy to accumulate, and only seconds for its release. But a main quake followed by weeks or months of aftershocks may be the typical way that energy caused by tectonic deformation is released. Geoscientists and mathematicians who research this idea suspect that the accumulation of energy over long periods may be reflected by the dissipation of energy over short periods, albeit abruptly. In other words, aftershocks are normal, and should be expected.

Shallow earthquakes are particularly prone to sequences of aftershocks, and the biggest aftershocks may approach the main quake in size. The destructive, magnitude 7.1 earthquake at Inangahua in 1968 had fifteen aftershocks greater than magnitude 5 within a month. It would take Auckland nearly a thousand years to clock up that amount of shaking.

The distressing sequence of Marlborough earthquakes in 1848 involved more than 150 shocks greater than magnitude 4.5 within three months. The main shock, estimated between magnitude 7.1 and 7.3, originated under the lower Awatere Valley (plate 6) and 150+ aftershocks were felt in Wellington some 65 km away. One can only marvel at the fortitude of the early settlers, unaccustomed to such natural hazards, as earthquakes are rare in Britain.

The potential for earthquake disasters to be compounded by aftershocks makes the study of earthquake patterns and sequences important for planning emergency services and for Civil Defence procedures. Buildings and structures weakened during an earthquake may collapse when subjected to just a wee bit more shaking during a smaller-magnitude aftershock.

Seismic activity and very large earthquakes produce both local earth deformation and ground shaking. The deformation includes the fault plane rupturing up to the surface and causing the surroundings to uplift, tilt, or drop down. Ground-shaking effects include liquefaction, landslides, ground cracking, tsunami, and damage to buildings, structures, and services such as electricity and sewerage.

Liquefaction occurs when water-saturated sediments temporarily lose strength because of ground shaking, and behave as a fluid. If liquefaction is severe, buildings may tilt or sink a bit, and underground pipes and tanks may float up to the surface. Such effects are rare with earthquakes that are magnitude 5 and less, but shaking can nevertheless cause a great deal of damage.

MAGNITUDES AND INTENSITIES

Two fundamentally different scales are used to describe earthquakes. The energy of an earthquake, released by the rupturing movement, is measured on a magnitude scale. The shaking and quaking that produces damaging effects at a particular place on the surface are measured on an intensity scale.

Earthquake magnitude

The magnitude of an earthquake is a measure of the actual wave energy released at the focus of the quake. It is directly measured by scientists from seismograms. The term 'magnitude' was chosen to indicate that the scale used to classify earthquake strength is similar to the scale used to describe the brightness of stars. Magnitude is a number derived from the amplitude of a seismograph recording of an earthquake, after it is corrected for the distance that the waves have travelled from the focus to the recording station. Charles Richter devised this way of measuring an earthquake's magnitude in order to compare the relative sizes of Californian quakes during the 1930s.

Because of the huge range of earthquake sizes, the magnitude scale is logarithmic. The amplitude of a seismograph recording of a magnitude 4 earthquake is ten times greater than that of a magnitude 3 earthquake at the same location. Even more startling, the energy released goes up not ten times, but about 32 times for each whole magnitude up the scale. In energy terms, a magnitude 8 quake releases nearly a million times more energy than a magnitude 4.

The largest earthquakes ever recorded had magnitudes greater than 9 on Richter's scale. Extremely small quakes, mainly of concern to people who need extremely stable working conditions, have negative magnitudes. The weakest magnitude that is felt by people is about magnitude 2. Houses and buildings are often damaged at magnitude 6, depending on local soil conditions, regional geology, and the depth and distance of the focus. Shallow earthquakes greater than magnitude 6 are capable of producing serious damage in a populated area. The seismic energy radiated by a magnitude 7.7 earthquake is equivalent to that released by a 50-megaton hydrogen bomb detonated underground.

Earthquake intensity

The intensity of an earthquake at a particular location is a measure of the degree of shaking at the surface. Intensity covers the local effects and the damage caused by the earthquake to people, animals, buildings, services, and structures in a particular environment. All these effects vary with distance from the earthquake's focus, and the greatest damage usually occurs closest to the epicentre. But the nature of the soil, subsoil, and rock beneath any particular place also has a substantial influence on the extent of shaking. After an earthquake occurs, scientists send out questionnaires and make a map of the intensities from the replies. The Modified Mercalli Intensity Scale is used to fix the limit of the intensity values. These are traditionally written in Roman numerals so that they will not be muddled with magnitude values.

Modified Mercalli Intensity Scale (MM)

The Modified Mercalli Intensity Scale measures the intensity of an earthquake, that is, its destructiveness caused by ground movement at a particular place. Town planners, insurance companies and regional authorities need to know the intensities of earthquakes likely to occur in particular areas. They also need to know how often the various levels of destruction will occur. The Modified Mercalli Intensity Scale adapted for New Zealand conditions was last updated in 1996, and it currently includes twelve steps.

The questionnaire distributed by seismologists to assess the intensity of an earthquake asks about the duration of the shaking, the observer's position, the construction materials of the building, the type of vehicle, the nature of the shock, the noises heard, and so on. Whether one is walking, standing, sitting, in a bed, car, truck, bus or train, makes a difference to the shaking intensity that is felt by individuals.

The questionnaire makes suggestions such as a jolt, vibration, or swaying for the nature of the shock, and offers boom, crack, and rumble as possible sound effects. For moderate and damaging shocks, questions about liquid spills (cups, baths, ponds), engineering structures (underground pipes, railways, bridges), fissures and cracks, abnormal movements in waterways (the sea, rivers, lakes), and building damage, are asked.

Modified Mercalli Intensity Scale (1996)

I   Not felt in general.

II   Felt by people at rest or on upper floors of buildings.

III   Felt indoors, hanging objects may swing slightly.

IV   Felt indoors by many, dishes rattle, walls may creak.

V   Felt outside, sleepers wakened, some crockery broken, hanging pictures move.

VI   Felt by everyone, furniture moves, plaster cracks, some minor chimney damage.

VII   General alarm, difficult to stand up, damage to weak masonry buildings, small slides and rock-falls, unrestrained water cylinders may move and leak, windows crack.

VIII   General alarm approaching panic, unreinforced chimneys fall, stone and brick walls damaged, possibly collapse, moderate landslides, ground cracks, liquefaction.

IX   Panic, serious damage to masonry buildings, some destroyed, many partially collapse, ground cracks, some houses shift off their foundations.

X   General panic, wooden buildings seriously damaged, landslides widespread, rivers slop over banks, severe liquefaction.

XI   General panic, broad ground cracks, soil slumps, great damage to underground pipes, few buildings remain standing.

XII   General panic, total destruction, objects thrown up in air.

When all the answers have been studied, the intensities are assessed and plotted on a map. Areas of equal intensity are then enclosed by an isoseismal line. Isoseismal lines work on the same principle as altitude contour lines on a topographic map and isobars on a weather map. An isoseismal map visually presents the extent of the effects of an earthquake, so it is valuable for estimating the size and location of historic quakes, and in calculating seismic hazards.

New Zealand's only isoseismal atlas (Downes, 1995) contains more than 120 major earthquake maps and includes information from eyewitnesses, contemporary diaries and newspapers, as well as modern scientific reports.

Richter and the magnitude scale

For seismologists, the most obvious indicator of an earthquake's strength is the size of the wiggle it makes on a seismograph record, a seismogram. Sadly, the length of time that recording continues is affected by the distance of the earthquake in a complicated way, but this is adjusted by clever maths so that magnitudes can be accurately compared. Ways of working out magnitude from the duration of shaking have also been found.

Amplitude and distance

The relationship between the maximum amplitude of the seismogram wiggle and distance is relatively simple. It was a measurement arbitrarily chosen by Charles Richter in 1935 for a magnitude scale that he designed to rank the shallow earthquakes in California, and adaptations of his system are now used worldwide for shallow quakes. Richter was working with standardised (and old-fashioned) seismographs, so he did not have to consider the sensitivities of different instruments. In fact, the type of instrument that he used has not been manufactured for nearly 40 years, and it bears little resemblance to modern technology.

Richter argued that if two earthquakes were at the same distance from a seismograph, it was reasonable to suppose that the bigger quake would have the bigger amplitude in its record. He then set about finding a way to allow for the effect of distance on the amplitude. As might be expected, Richter found that an earthquake produced bigger amplitudes on seismographs near its epicentre than on those further away, and he established a rule-of-thumb to allow for the reduction in amplitude caused by distance. By applying this rule he could, in effect, bring all earthquakes to a standard distance from the seismograph for comparison.

Problems of the enormous range of amplitudes that earthquakes produce were overcome by defining the scale in terms of the logarithm of the amplitude, instead of the amplitude itself. It is measured in thousandths of a millimetre. For convenience, Richter adopted a standard earthquake so small that he did not expect smaller ones to be of much interest, and called this an earthquake of magnitude zero. However, the scale can cope with quakes smaller than magnitude zero by using negative magnitudes. There is no upper limit to the scale either, although quakes of magnitude 10 or more have not been recorded in historic times. This is indeed fortunate, because a magnitude 9.6 earthquake releases more than one thousand times the energy of the quake that rocked Taiwan in 1999.

In principle, Richter's scale did no more than provide a systematic way of ranking shallow earthquakes in a given area as large, moderate, or small. In practice it has been found to correlate loosely with the amount of seismic energy that has been released. This loose correlation with seismic energy has made his idea very useful. New ways of determining magnitude are continually being introduced to provide a scale for deep earthquakes and modern types of seismograph, and to improve the accuracy of estimating the amount of seismic energy released.

Mathematical models that reconcile the amount of released energy and the magnitude have been refined, and distinctions have been made between wave energy and total elastic energy. While the rule-of-thumb is that M8 quakes are nearly a million times bigger than M4, a more accurate statement is that an M8 releases nearly a million times more energy than an M4 in wave energy.

Is there one true magnitude?

No. Different mathematical formulas and magnitude scales are used depending on the size of the quake, the depth of its focus, and the distance of the epicentre from recording seismographs. They measure different parts of the radiation pattern of earthquakes; all methods have some limitations, and no one method is used to measure the magnitude for all types of earthquake.

Correlations between a value for earthquake magnitude and a value for ground-shaking intensity are a bit dicey. This is mainly because felt intensity is strongly dependent on the particular ground, rock types and geological structure of a given area, as well as the distance from the epicentre and the depth of the focus. Therefore, comparisons can only give the expected maximum intensity for the area immediately around the epicentre.

Table 1 Comparisons of scales of local magnitude (M_L) and epicentre intensity for shallow earthquakes within the crust of the earth.

Magnitude	Intensity at epicentre	Intensity effects
M_L3	MMIII	Felt indoors
M_L4	MMIV–V	Felt by most people
M_L5	MMVI–VII	Felt by everyone, minor to moderate damage
M_L6	MMVII–VIII	Damage moderate to minor
M_L7	MMIX–X	Major damage

The different magnitude ratings that result from the various calculations are critical to understanding earth processes at an advanced scientific level. They are of little value to the public, however, because no magnitude rating indicates the destructiveness of an earthquake. That is, a magnitude number does not report the amount of chaos in neighbourhoods near the epicentre.

For example, the 1994 Northridge California, and the 1995 Kobe Japan earthquakes had similar magnitudes, but 53 Californians died whereas the Kobe quake caused 5300 deaths. The differences in earthquake destructiveness were mainly due to local soil conditions, regional geology, and the style of house construction. Furthermore, Japan has had 26 earthquakes this century of greater magnitude than that at Kobe, but only one of them caused more deaths.

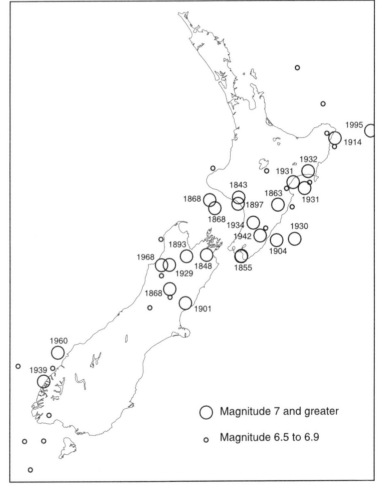

Figure 8 New Zealand's largest shallow earthquakes since 1840 incidentally show up the silliness of persisting with a 'Richter Scale'. Obviously, few earthquakes before the 1950s had their wave amplitudes captured by a seismo- graph and, as magnitude 7 quakes release 30 times more energy than magnitude 6s, a very small measurement error (perhaps 6.9 instead of 7.0) can distort the pattern.

To measure magnitude, modern scientists use many methods including combinations of field geology, geodetics, and seismology. Sophisticated surveying techniques and boots-in-the-mud fieldwork bring details of historical quakes to light. This map includes measurements based on several magnitude scales — none of which is called 'Richter'.

○ Magnitude 7 and greater

o Magnitude 6.5 to 6.9

Media reports that persist with 'Richter' scales are irrelevant to people wanting to know how bad the damage is and how the local community is likely to cope. Seismologists and geologists do not actually calculate Richter's magnitudes in the way that Richter did, and only use 'Richter' when pushed by news media. Geoscientists then give reporters the 'local magnitude'.

Local magnitude

The local magnitude (M_L) is based on the systematic decrease of wave amplitude with distance. Nowadays it is mainly used by seismologists for relatively close, smallish, and shallow earthquakes. Only earthquakes with focal depths less than 15 km, magnitudes less than 6.5, and epicentres within 600 km of recording stations are suitable for M_L readings.

Values from numerous recording stations have to be averaged to give a reliable M_L because earthquake waves radiate at varying intensities and rates in different directions due to differences in regional rock types and geological structures.

Local magnitude is calculated from the logarithm of the maximum trace amplitude, measured in thousandths of a millimetre, on a standard Wood-Anderson seismograph located on firm ground 100 km from the epicentre. The maximum trace of amplitude from an M_L4 earthquake located 100 km from a Wood-Anderson seismograph is 10 mm. This measure is used as a reference event for other calculations, and corrections to a reference distance allow direct comparisons of logarithmic amplitudes. Every time the amplitude increases by a factor of 10, the M_L increases by one.

Body-wave magnitude

The body-wave magnitude (m_b) has a different set of geophysical calculations, and is used to assess the energy given out from deep but smallish earthquakes. It is based on the maximum amplitude of a P-wave with a period of about one second. This becomes more distinctive with distance from the source, and m_b can be used to characterise the size of an earthquake globally. Body-wave magnitude measurements are the most accurate way to size earthquakes that are less than magnitude 6 and originate more than 60 km under the surface, but differences of ±0.3 are not uncommon, and extensive averaging and correcting are often necessary.

Surface-wave magnitude

The surface-wave magnitude (M_S) is based on the largest amplitudes of a surface-wave sequence propagated by moderate to large, distant, and shallow quakes. Earthquakes originating near deep-sea trenches that are felt around the world are appropriate candidates for M_S calculations. It is only good for magnitudes up to 7.3 as thereafter it becomes saturated. It is not useful for deep quakes either, because they do not generate surface waves, and no mathematical corrections yet devised seem appropriate.

In fact, magnitude values from M_L, m_b, and M_S measurements are the same only for small earthquakes with very short lengths of rupture. Large, shallow earthquakes often rupture rock up to the surface, and where the length of the rupture is much greater than the wavelengths used in calculating magnitude, the scale becomes saturated. As a result, these magnitude measurements are neither appropriate nor accurate for large earthquakes with surface ruptures over tens and hundreds of kilometres. They cannot distinguish large earthquakes based on the amplitude of a particular wave on a seismogram.

Moment magnitude

A more physically based magnitude, moment magnitude (M_W) involves the average slip movement over the ruptured part of the fault, the rupture area, and the strength of the rock. Moment magnitude measures energy radiated from the entire rupture surface, not just that radiated from a point of origin — the focus of the earthquake. It has been used over the last twenty years and is the method that seismologists favour because it can be used for all depths, and for moderate to extremely large earthquakes.

Moment magnitude is based on the logarithmic scaling of seismic moments. It can be independently estimated by techniques from both surveying and field geology because it is a function of the area of the fault's rupture plane, the strength of the rock (the shear modulus of elasticity) and the amount of offset.

Large earthquakes resulting from about a metre of displacement on faults more than 30 km long and 15 km deep have M_W values of about 7. Earthquakes involving longer faults and greater displacement have higher M_W magnitudes. For example, the 1960 Chilean earthquake involved 30 metres of offset over a 1000-km long fault so its magnitude is M_W9.5. Some clever soul has also figured out that an earthquake that caused a fault to rupture right around the world would have a magnitude of M_W10.6. Such a rupture is considered a wild improbability.

All this rather puts paid to the idea of the 'open-ended' scale so beloved of the media. Reporting that an earthquake measures XYZ on the open-ended Richter scale is only marginally less silly than saying its epicentre was XYZ kilometres away on the open-ended distance scale. And, if you want to know how much the ground shook or how much damage occured, ask for the intensity of the earthquake.

FAULTS AND FRAILTIES

Geological faults may be active for millions of years. They remain zones of weakness that repeatedly rupture and create earthquakes, often regardless of changes in tectonic forces. Active faults are, however, a tiny proportion of the total faults apparent from the geological record and from scars in the landscape. If you have taken a sneak peek at figures 17 to 20, and are quietly panicking over retirement plans, fear not. Most faults are inactive — compare them with figure 13. Some of New Zealand's most impressive geological faults have provided the safety valve for deformation caused by compressional, extensional, and lateral stresses at different times during their history of repeated rupturing.

Because tectonic plates tend to move at constant speeds for long periods of geological time (although at different speeds in different directions), earthquakes on faults tend to occur at roughly regular intervals. Most earthquakes result from ruptures along existing fault planes and, as the damaging movements are repeats of earlier performances, studying faults gives good information about the likely style of their next rupturing presentation.

The rupture of rock in a large, shallow earthquake often reaches the surface and distorts the landscape. The visible edge of crustal ruptures is the fault 'trace'; often marked by a change in slope or a long bank (a fault scarp). Streams with right-angled corners, lines of 'sag' ponds, and series of lined-up notches in hills also indicate fault traces and, therefore, former crustal earthquakes. Subduction and deep-slab earthquakes do not create fault traces.

Geologists have become accustomed to curving and bumpy fault 'planes', although some find them too much to warrant the term 'plane', and refer to the interface between displaced bodies of rock as the fault 'surface'. Either way, while a fault plane is seldom smooth or straight, please remember it is definitely a two-dimensional surface with a significant depth as well as length. To complicate the matter further, many fault 'planes' have a variable, but definite, thickness. Rock adjacent to the fault may become so crushed, shattered and generally minced, that it develops a character all of its own, with very little resemblance to the material that it developed from (back cover photograph).

Visible fault traces can be so spectacular that it is easy to forget that they are merely the top edge of a rupture surface that extends for kilometres underground. Fault traces may be hundreds of kilometres long, but their rupture planes seldom extend more than about 15 km downwards, and they are nearly always associated with crustal earthquakes.

The dominance of either extension, compression, or lateral stress creates particular types of geological fault that displace rocks on either side of the fault plane in different ways. Where a fault plane is not vertical, the rock mass overlying the fault is called the 'hanging wall'; the 'footwall' is beneath the fault plane.

Normal faults

Extension stresses that stretch the crust of the earth create 'normal' faults when the rocks rupture. Regions with normal faults are often characterised by high crustal heat-flow, earthquakes, earthquake swarms, and often by volcanism — which sums up the Taupo–Rotorua region nicely. It might be thought that the incoming Pacific Plate subducting under the area would cause the overlying crust to crumple and thicken under compressive stresses but, as is quite common behind deep-sea trenches, the overlying Australian Plate is moving away from the trench and a 'back-arc' basin is developing. This basin has all the classic extensional-stress hallmarks — thin crust, high heat-flow, volcanism, geothermal activity, normal faults, and shallow earthquakes.

The horizontal distance between points on opposite sides of a normal fault increases with movement along the plane (figure 9). The size and orientation of the slip vector between two previously contiguous points across the fault is the geological 'offset'. The procedures for calculating this offset result in all sorts of information about the general displacement and deformation in the region.

The slope of a normal fault plane generally varies around 60°. The Taupo Volcanic Zone hosts New Zealand's most active normal faults, as the people of Edgecumbe can well testify. It is perhaps fortunate that the zone's crust is too thin and hot for individual faults to generate earthquakes with magnitudes greater than 7. Normal fault planes may have numerous kinks and curves as the Edgecumbe fault trace shows (plates 46 to 48), and their angle of dip can vary in different segments, and at different depths, of the fault.

Normal faults are so-called because they were the 'normal' types of fault observed in the coalfields of Europe during the nineteenth century. Every so often someone would note a fault with the opposite sense of movement — and call it a reverse fault. Normal faults are sometimes referred to as dip-slip faults because rock on one side slips down the sloping face of the fault plane, that is, the hanging wall slips down the footwall. But dip-slip also describes movement caused by compressional stress, where rock on one side is rammed up the dipping face of the fault plane. Accordingly, dip-slip is reserved to describe a rupturing movement, not a type of fault.

Reverse faults

Reverse faults and the peculiar behaviour that pushes older rocks on top of younger rocks, as in the European Alps, stimulated the study of earth deformation during the nineteenth century. It was not until the 1970s, however, when the theory of plate tectonics provided global explanations for the various stress regimes, that the rupture patterns of reverse faults were accounted for on a regional basis.

The horizontal distance between points on opposite sides of a reverse fault becomes closer because of slip along the fault. Rock on one side moves up the dipping face of the fault plane as tectonic forces compress the area. That is, the hanging-wall rock mass moves upward with respect to the footwall. Reverse faults often slope more shallowly than normal faults, and where their fault planes dip less than 45°, they are classified as thrust faults (figure 9).

New Zealand has several regions of largely reverse faults where compression is, or has been, the dominant deforming force. Largely reverse-movement faults parallel the Hikurangi Trough off the east coast of the North Island in a narrow onshore strip. The effort of convection forces pulling the oceanic plate down the trough crumples and compresses the edge of the overlying Australian Plate, and the offshore area out to the trough is also striped with reverse faults parallel to the trough.

On the Pacific Plate side of the Alpine Fault in the South Island, compressive forces and reverse faults have created the range and basin topography of Central Otago where five major valleys are roughly parallel and separated by fault-block ranges. Reverse faults in the Nelson area hosted the tragic Murchison earthquake in 1929, and the Inangahua quake in 1968.

However, many of the country's faults with a strong reverse-slip component are caused by oblique forces and include horizontal slip as well. New Zealand's most spectacular reverse-fault movements are strongly related to horizontal stress and lateral movement along the Alpine Fault. This transform plate boundary is activated by stress from plate convergence at an oblique angle to the zone of weakness; or as scientists say, 'The relative plate-motion

Figure 9 Normal fault: rock above the fault plane slips down the dip because of extension stress. Reverse fault: rock above the fault plane is forced up the dip by compression. Strike-slip fault: horizontal displacement — left-lateral in this case. Rock is separated by an almost vertical fault plane. Normal + strike-slip fault: most faults combine some vertical and horizontal movement because locally the dominant stresses are seldom exactly horizontal or vertical.

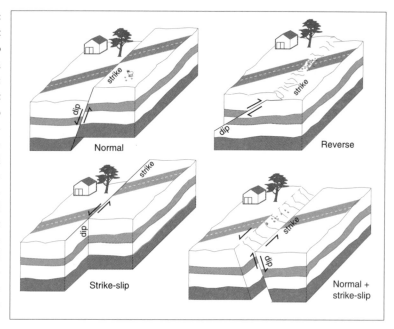

slip-vector is more than 30°.' Consequently, compressive and horizontal forces both play a part in the dramatic (and picturesque) deformation of the region.

Nearly all reverse faults are affected by some degree of stress that offsets rock on either side of the fault plane in a lateral direction. This is because the location of a rupture plane is heavily influenced by the rock's physical characteristics, which depend on its origins, and its childhood or adolescent behaviours under previous tectonic regimes. Furthermore, rupture planes seldom develop exactly at 45° to the direction of greatest stress.

Reverse faults adjust regional compression and normal faults accommodate extension, so 'reverse' is a rational sort of label given that the opposite force creates normal faults. It does not, however, suggest that something is moving backwards. Recent displacement along reverse faults is often difficult to recognise in the field because their traces are almost never straight, and they may pose as gently rolling ridges or be confused with abandoned river terraces.

Strike-slip faults

Strike-slip faults occur in a wide range of sizes, and in almost any tectonic environment. At oceanic ridges, at zones of oceanic plate convergence, and at collision zones between continents, strike-slip faults transform movement from one extensional or compressional zone to another. Where strike-slip faults are part of the plate boundary, they are referred to as transform faults. Transform faults are commonly hundreds to thousands of kilometres long.

Major strike-slip faults on a lesser scale also occur within plates because of compressional, extensional, or lateral shearing on a regional basis. The different strengths, densities and internal structures of different types of rocks are strong players in regional deformation.

Strike-slip faults are defined as those on which the major displacement is horizontal; that is, the slip is parallel to the strike of the fault. Those with purely strike-slip movement (not terribly common) are activated when the major stress is both horizontal and at 45° to the fault plane (figure 9). This shearing stress produces sideways movement, so that rocks on the two sides of the fault are displaced laterally with respect to each other. Where the stress field diverges from this attitude, some dip-slip actions develop. Strike-slip faults are described as right-lateral or left-lateral, depending on the direction of movement when viewed from the opposite side of the fault. This is very convenient terminology because it doesn't matter on which side of the fault you are standing (you can test this for yourself using the strike-slip sketch in figure 9).

Faults created primarily by the stress field that produces purely lateral movements have nearly vertical fault planes, so their dips approach 90°. Most strike-slip faults, however, incorporate elements of compressional or extensional stress, if not within the modern tectonic system, then at some distant time in the mists of antiquity. As a result, absolutely vertical fault planes are something of a rarity. The fault traces of strike-slip faults are often longer and straighter than those of normal and reverse faults, but overlapping and offset segments that have the same general direction are common. Much of the eastern half of the North Island copes with tectonic stress by deforming along strike-slip faults.

Strike-slip faults suffer a variety of names including lateral, transcurrent and wrench faults. To add to the jumble, these faults have the same sense of movement as transform faults, but this last tag is mostly reserved for a chunk of plate boundary.

Dips and strikes

All the names for strike-slip faults, along with the normal, dip-slip, reverse, and thrust labels, have been useful at some time in the development of, or pertinent to some aspect of, earth-deformation studies and seismology. The concepts of strike and dip, however, are fairly standard among geoscientists. Their numerical expression orientates a geological structure in space, regardless of the language or culture of particular geoscientists.

Dip is the standard geological term for the slope of a more-or-less planar geological feature and it can be considered in the same way that 'slope' is used to describe hillsides. For example, New Zealand's steepest city street, Baldwin Street in Dunedin, dips at 20° in the top part of the street, 17° in the middle, and 'flattens out' to a mere 14° at the bottom. The top part of the street is paved with concrete rather than asphalt — presumably because asphalt might slip down the dip on a hot day.

Strike is used geologically in the same way that sailors use 'bearing'; it is the direction of a horizontal line. The strike direction can be plotted on a map with respect to north for any roughly planar surface, such as a geological fault plane. It is the same orientation that the water line of a lake makes on its shore or, indeed, any line of still water on an adjacent surface. Finding the strike of a kitchen-sink is a good start for do-it-yourselfers.

To complete the orientation of a fault plane, the angle of the dip and the direction that it faces are needed. The dip is always measured at right angles to strike — which is a horizontal measure by definition. When the direction that the dip faces is added, the fault plane can be completely identified and orientated in space, and shown by a symbol on a map.

For example, if a fault trace strikes at 045°, it is easy to understand that the top edge of the fault plane heads northeast across the countryside. Similarly, a geological structure that strikes at 045° and dips 70° to the southeast can be imagined as a coldish and extremely steep bank (only good for growing ferns in New Zealand conditions). If this structure were a fault plane, and described as a strike-slip fault, we would know that the direction of the earth-quaking lurch was both horizontal and parallel to the fault plane.

This hypothetical fault plane is technically described as 045/70SE, which tells us that one side of the fault moved northeast while the other side moved exactly southwest. If it were further described as a right-lateral fault (imagine that the side of the trace that you are standing on stays still relative to the opposite side), the countryside on the far side lurches to your right.

Lost in space

For people without experience of compasses, here's the procedure. There are 360° in a circle, and due north is assigned the 000° label and the 12 o'clock position. Numbers increase clockwise around the circle, so due east is 090°, south is 180°, and west is 270°. If you think you are heading due north but are actually wobbling two degrees off course to the west, your bearing (that is, your strike) would be 358°.

PALEOSEISMOLOGY

Because most earthquakes are associated with fault ruptures, faults can be considered as geological seismographs (meteorite impacts and volcanic activity may also produce earthquakes). Faults may record events over as much as the last 500,000 years but, in most cases, the record is shorter because of landscape erosion. Nevertheless, this is a welcome advance on the time covered by daily newspapers and, indeed, by written records anywhere in the world.

New Zealand's earthquake-generating faults have been fairly quiet since historical records began, and even quieter since the advent of reliable seismographs. The averaged time-gap between large earthquakes on some local faults is a hundred times longer than our written history, which makes geological detective work on ancient earthquakes socially and economically important.

This research has four aims: where past quakes occurred, how big they were, what type of faulting was involved, and how often they recurred. Patterns of recurring quakes in region X, recurrence intervals between quakes on fault Y, and the size of quakes on fault Z are collected. This information is used to estimate the size and the timing of future earthquakes, and it becomes the basis for the mitigation plans that are a legal requirement for local and regional authorities in high-risk areas.

The branch of geoscience that deals with the location, size and timing of past earthquakes is paleoseismology. It works on the supposition that active faults release energy in earthquakes of a particular size, and that quakes of roughly the same size might recur with some regularity. Theoretically, this means that average recurrence intervals can be calculated from faults' rupture lengths, displacement increments, and slip rates. The probability that some faults produce earthquakes in clusters is supported by paleoseismological research. Consequently, the regularity of recurrence is more a theoretical yardstick than a cause for a diary note by the time geoscientists have finished accounting for all the variables.

Paleoseismologists mostly focus on the sedimentary records of earth-quaking ruptures and the deformation of landforms, rather than on crustal movements over millions of years. They study earthquake patterns through fieldwork on fault-plane displacements, and develop computer models to create future scenarios.

Geological fault planes, however, are not easy to access or understand. Methods are fine-tuned through investigating recent and nineteenth-century quakes where the date, the intensities felt, the surface rupture, and the distribution of ground-shaking responses, such as landslides, are known. Almost all the types of geological and topographical features used to assess prehistoric earthquakes were originally identified following historic earthquakes. The principles that 'the past is the key to the future' and 'the present is the key to the past' underlie much paleoseismology. Consequently, paleoseismologists are well represented at scenes of earthquake disruption, looking for fresh geological patterns and processes that might be recognised and preserved in rocks and landforms.

Earth deformation geologists examine rocks and landforms to determine how often faulting occurred in the past, how much movement took place, and the rates of earth deformation (plates 19, 32 and 71). Several methods are used to assess magnitudes of prehistoric earthquakes. They may be calculated by comparing the length of the surface rupture with those on worldwide databases for movements associated with modern earthquakes. Where the area of a prehistoric rupture plane can be estimated, the energy released during the rupturing earthquake can be converted to a moment magnitude (M_W). Total movement within a known period may also be divided by the number of movements in order to assess prehistoric magnitudes. Studies of modern earthquakes indicate that only moderately large and shallow earthquakes — those greater than magnitude 6.5 — leave reliable fault traces that are responsive to paleoseismic investigations. Unfortunately the opposite doesn't hold. The focal depth of the magnitude 7.1 earthquake at Loma Prieta, California in 1989 was only 12 km, but it did not produce a surface rupture.

The frequency of earthquakes is calculated by dating features and organic materials that have been disturbed by earthquakes, often using techniques such as radioisotope and radiocarbon dating. A faulting event is always younger than the youngest material that it disturbs, and older than the oldest undisrupted material that covers it. So, if the youngest disturbed material is radiocarbon dated to 2100±70 years ago, we know that the rupture occurred after this. If the rupture area was then conveniently covered with volcanic ash dated at 1950±40 years ago, the earthquake can be given a probable date range — some time between 1950 and 2100 years ago. Many dates are needed before a reliable pattern for the recurrence of earthquakes on a particular fault can be seen.

Offsets at faults are measured in two main ways. The first involves digging trenches and investigating a cross-section view of the fault. The displacement of the rock and soil layers on either side of a fault can be precisely measured and reliably interpreted, especially where the stratigraphy is rich, varied, and exposed. Investigating fault displacements through stratigraphic offsets in a trench has an advantage over landform offsets inasmuch as the climate, forestry and farming practices, or beasts with two or four legs, have not kicked around the evidence. Tree roots and burrows, however, complicate the picture.

These days, ditchdiggers or bulldozers generally excavate trenches. Even so, they are no deeper than 5 metres for safety reasons, which means that they are restricted to the fault's stratigraphic history shown in the top 5 metres of geological deposits. If these deposits span 50,000 years of geological activity, there is great delight among the workers, but they usually have to settle for much less. Of course, on a very active fault, the movements of the last 5000 years may answer many of their questions regarding the amount, direction, and timing of ruptures during that period. Unfortunately, the dip of faults tends to vary near the surface, and a regional picture requires several trenches and drill cores.

Evidence of ground shaking, as opposed to fault-plane rupture, can also be picked up stratigraphically in trenches as sand dikes, load structures in soft sediments, density-current deposits, and signs of liquefaction. Picking the spot to dig a trench is critical to the success of the research. Flattish surfaces with little vegetation, strata with low permeability (so that ground-shaking responses such as sand dikes can survive), a steady water table, dateable layers (for example, layers of peat or fossils), and a lack of local bunnies are all positive features. Paleoseismologists need sites where the earthquake features have been quickly buried and protected from processes that erode or disturb the evidence. A series of drill cores is taken for deeper studies (plate 32).

The second major line of enquiry useful for investigating both vertical and horizontal displacements involves the offset of landforms. Such landforms include streams, river terraces, uplifted former shorelines, truncated hill spurs, and fault scarps — the long and usually straight banks that separate the upside from the downside of a fault plane. Fault scarps are ancient surface ruptures that mark the fault trace and, although they undoubtedly developed simultaneously with large earthquakes, they fall to pieces with time. Depending on the local climate, topography, and population, scarps have a short shelf life, and are only helpful for assessing large-scale displacements. Within a few hundred years a sharp, vertical, metre-high scarp may have degraded into a gently rounded slope, covered with soil, gravel or rocks.

The offset of outcropping rock types, the displacement of rivers, and the development of sag ponds can provide information covering millions of years of a fault's history, but it is tricky to take precise measurements relating to particular events. Mapping the distribution of ground-shaking features topographically indicates the earthquake's intensity, but sand boils, small landslides, fissures, and vegetation disturbances seldom survive the passage of time. Series of landslides that face the same direction and tsunami deposits also point to seismic shaking.

Elevated shorelines and drowned tidal marshes are strong indicators of regional uplift or subsidence. At the Pakarae River mouth, north of Gisborne, seven uplifted beaches are arranged in a staircase fashion. The highest (and oldest) is 24 metres above sea level and nearly 7000 years old. Radiocarbon dates and careful deformation measurements show that the vertical displacement of the coast caused by each earthquake was 2 to 4 metres. Similar beach terraces at Mahia Peninsula (plate 31) and near East Cape record significant uplift along faults in the crust that parallel the Hikurangi Trough. Each uplift event was probably caused by an earthquake greater than magnitude 7.5.

Turakirae Head near Wellington (plate 20) has four marine terraces that record four great earthquakes in the last 8000 years. The most recent was the 1855 Wairarapa earthquake, which uplifted the beach a maximum of 6.4 metres. The previous rupture, about 2500 years ago, lifted its beach 9.13 metres at the highest point. The third terrace was lifted a maximum of 5.51 metres about 5000 years ago, and 7200 years ago the beach was raised 3 metres. A strong relationship between the size of uplift and the time elapsed since the previous event suggests that the uplift is related to the amount of deformation energy that has accumulated. Profiles of the terraces have been surveyed all around Turakirae Head, and geoscientists consider that earthquakes similar in size to the 1855 quake accompanied most of the uplift events.

Rates calculated from landform offsets across faults are averaged to millimetres a year, but there may be thousands of years between major earthquaking movements. Intervals between quakes are calculated by dating volcanic ash, fossils or glacial deposits that have been displaced by the rupturing movement.

Historical earthquakes under steep forested terrain cause extensive tree destruction, and tree-rings, the age distributions of lichen and other biological analyses are proving useful as additional ways of dating such disturbances. The amount of displacement per major earthquake, coupled with regional deformation rates, provides another method to investigate an average recurrence interval for the faulting, and hence for the quake associated with it.

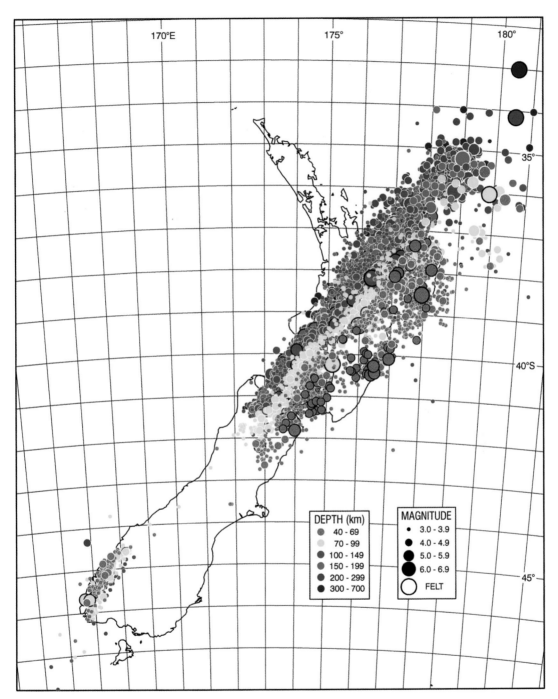

Map 1 New Zealand's deep earthquakes become deeper from east to west under the North Island, reflecting the westward dip of the subducting Pacific Plate. Under Fiordland the earthquakes become deeper towards the east, which reflects the eastwards dip of the subducting Australian Plate. Note the lack of deep earthquakes under the Alpine Fault and the south and east of the South Island — this is because neither plate subducts under this area.

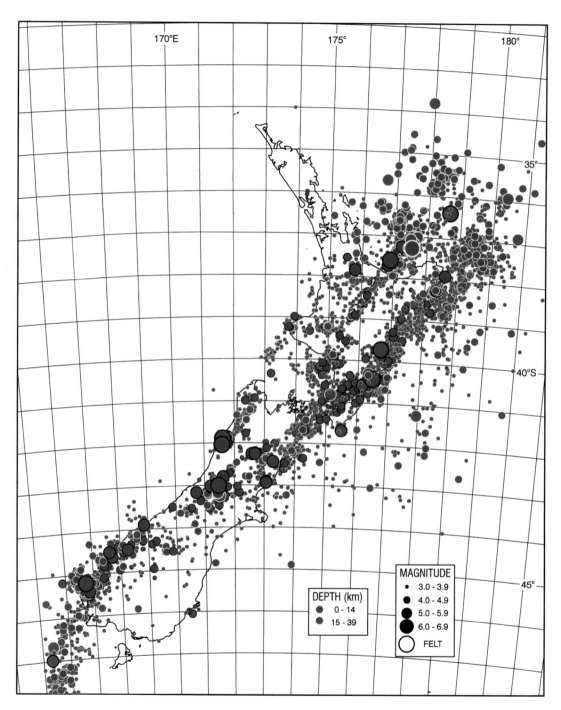

Map 2 Shallow earthquakes under the North Island's East Coast are subduction earthquakes caused by the downward bending of the Pacific Plate. Similarly, those under Fiordland are caused by the bending of the Australian Plate as it subducts. The large earthquakes in Marlborough and Canterbury are the products of distributed crustal deformation associated with the plate boundary, but none occur on the Alpine Fault. Quakes in the Taupo Volcanic Zone result from extensional stresses resulting in rock ruptures in the overlying Australian crust.

Plate 1 The Glenroy River in the Nelson Lakes National Park flows along the Alpine Fault. View northwards with Mt Cann and the igneous rocks of the Australian Plate on the left. Softer metamorphic rocks of the Pacific Plate (right) develop fans of erosion debris that push the river westwards against the igneous rocks.

Plate 2 The Alpine Fault (bottom left to lower right) blunts the slopes of Red Hill Range in western Otago. View southwards from the Australian Plate towards the Red Mountain (centre), with the almost vertically tilted schists of the Pacific Plate behind.

Plate 3 The southernmost part of the Alpine Fault as it runs out to sea just north of Milford Sound. View southwest across the Kaipo Slip, which has occurred in rocks crushed and shattered by movements along the fault (see back cover photograph).

Plate 4 West of Hillersden in the middle part of the Wairau Valley, the Alpine Fault has a straight, strong and single trace (arrowed from bottom).

Plate 5 The Alpine Fault down the Wairau Valley, about 35 km from the coast, has two roughly parallel active strands (arrowed at bottom right). These are marked by trenches, ponds, and offset stream-channels. View to the northeast.

Plate 6 The Awatere Fault Zone at Tarndale in the Nelson Lakes National Park. Water-filled depressions along the fault traces are the tarns, less poetically referred to as sag ponds by scientists. At least five fault segments are traceable on the ground. A landslide, probably triggered by an earthquake, covers a major trace at the upper left.

Plate 7 The Clarence Fault disrupts the slope of the Inland Kaikoura Range. The dark grey mudstone of the mountains has been thrust upwards along the fault, and is at least 100 million years older than the fossil-rich calcareous siltstone on the down-side of the fault. View northeast along the valley of the Clarence River.

Plate 8 The last onshore expression of the Hope Fault as it marks the edge of the Seaward Kaikoura Range and runs out to sea just north of Kaikoura — the peninsula is just visible at the right. The Clarence Fault strikes across the flanks of the Inland Kaikoura Range, top left.

Plate 9 Geologist Alexander McKay standing on the right-lateral offset of the Hope Fault during the late nineteenth century. Strike-slip movement on this fault created the 1888 North Canterbury earthquake, and offset the fence to the right by 2.6 metres. The fault runs left to right across the photograph in line with the extra piece of fence that McKay is standing against.

Plate 10 The Hope Fault blunts the foothills of the Hawk Range and has offset (from left) Green Burn, Sawyers Creek and Kahutara River. The snow-capped Dillon Cone is in the Inland Kaikoura Range, which is bounded by the roughly parallel Clarence and Awatere faults.

Plate 11 Wellington's natural harbour formed as the sea flooded between two uplifted blocks of crust. Miramar Peninsula was probably an island 600 years ago, before an earthquake lifted the Kilbirnie area. The Wellington Fault runs from bottom left to top right, and eventually finishes at the Manawatu Gorge. The geological structure continues, however, as the Mohaka Fault (see plates 24, 28 and 33).

Plate 12 View southwards of the Wellington Fault exposed in the Hutt River, Upper Hutt. A 7-metre-wide broken and shattered zone of fault breccia and gouge is exposed for about 200 metres south to the Silverstream Bridge, just visible in the distance.

Plate 13 The Wellington Fault begins off the southern coast, separates Wellington's western suburbs of Karori and Northland (on the right) from Kelburn and Highbury, and continues past the city's Botanical Gardens (bottom left). The splendid 'sag ponds' are actually highly engineered dams for the city water supply.

Plate 14 The scarp of the Wellington Fault dominates the Hutt Valley, which has had river sediments deposited in it to several hundred metres in depth. View westwards with the Porirua Harbour and Kapiti Island at the right, Cook Strait, and in the distance the Marlborough Sounds.

Plate 15 Long Gully is the wilderness area in the top centre of plate 13. Looking westwards over the Long Gully segment of the Wellington Fault. The most recent movement along this part of the strike-slip fault was 300–500 years ago, and some dip-slip is evident.

Plate 16 The Wellington Fault blunts the foothills east of the Tararua Range, west of Pahiatua. The fault finishes by name at the Manawatu Gorge, but the structure continues northwards to the Bay of Plenty. Note the right-lateral offset of the creeks.

Plate 17 View eastwards over the mainly strike-slip Ohariu Fault in the northern Ohariu Valley. The fault runs left to right across the middle of the photograph just below the blue-roofed house. The uplifted side (bottom) has disrupted the drainage, and a pond has developed east of the fault. The farmer dug the straight ditch to drain the swampy area. The light-coloured patches across the road are golf-course greens.

Plate 18 The fault-controlled Otaihanga Valley, east of Paraparaumu, is probably a northern strand of the Ohariu Fault, and this segment is considered active.

Plate 19 Midwinter mud for paleoseismologists working in a trench across the Ohariu Fault. Reverse movement on this part of the fault has thrust dark greywacke, which is more than 200 million years old, over gravels, sand, and silt deposited during the last 100,000 years. Radiocarbon dates from the trench indicate that the latest movement occured less than 1200 years ago.

Plate 20 The Wellington coast at the end of the Rimutaka Range has been uplifted in a series of earth-quaking ruptures over the last 2500 years. Rocky Turakirae Head has several ancient beaches stranded well above the wave level. Three large, flat hill terraces (centre) are former beaches that were uplifted 100,000 to 350,000 years ago. The Baring Head Fault runs through the gully at the left.

Plate 22 The vertical fault plane of a strike-slip segment of the Wairarapa Fault in the Rimutaka Range east of Petone. The grey metamorphic rock is at least 140 million years old, but the river gravels on the left have been deposited within the last 10,000 years.

Plate 21 Looking northeast over Featherston and along the trace of the Wairarapa Fault (arrowed). Displaced and dog-legged streams are common features along this fault as they cross over from the uplifted ranges.

Plate 23 The uplift and right-lateral strike-slip components of the Wairarapa Fault are clear as they cross and offset ancient river terraces of the Waiohine River. The fault runs from bottom left to centre right. The rupturing events would have been accompanied by massive earthquakes.

Plate 24 View northwards along part of the Mohaka Fault, the continuation of the Wellington Fault, inland from Hastings. This mainly right-lateral strike-slip fault has some vertical displacement, and the scarp, up to 6 metres high in places, faces uphill. The straight trace over hilly topography indicates a steeply dipping fault plane.

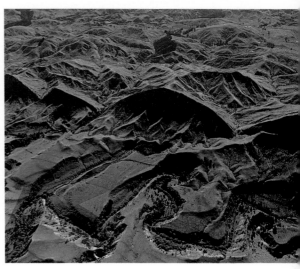

Plate 26 The bluffs of Silver Range south of Hastings. View eastwards over the Hawea Stream shows at least four parallel fault traces that are probably northern continuations of the Adam–Tinui Fault system. Further strands of faults are visible in the distance—seek, find, and count!

Plate 25 This hill-facing scarp on the Kaweka Range is not the top edge of an active fault plane, but a 'ridge-rent'. Such rents are probably associated with the area being shaken along existing structural weaknesses in a rock mass during an earthquake.

Plate 27 View northeast to Waipukerau showing the active Waipukerau Fault Zone, which is the northern extension of the Wairarapa Fault. Here, there are multiple strands, and the zone is a mixture of growing folds and fault scarps. The area used to be a series of flat river terraces that have been uplifted and deformed over the last 100,000 years. The ridges provided high ground above swampy land for the early settlers — their choice of settlement spot has yet to be tested.

Plate 28 A classic sag pond on the trace of the Mohaka Fault. The fault plane is nearly vertical at this site. The latest movements have uplifted the left side, but previous ruptures lifted the right side, so the rock along the fault plane is well shattered.

Plate 29 View northwards of the Desert Road, the Whanga-ehu River, the irregular and erosion-modified scarp of the Rangipo Fault, and Mt Rua-pehu at top left. Wahianoa Aqueduct (bottom) runs from southern Ruapehu to Lake Moawhango through a tunnel under the road. Collapses of the sheared rock of the Rangi-po Fault plane delayed work when the tunnel was being built.

Plate 30 The Martha Hill gold–silver mine is surrounded by the town of Waihi. View northeast across the now inactive Waihi Fault Zone. The trace (left of the mine) is only known from magnetic, gravity and electrical resistivity data, because the area is thickly covered with volcanic materials.

Plate 31 The Mahia Peninsula juts into northern Hawke Bay. This oblique view to the west, towards Wairoa, shows at least six raised beaches. The four more-or-less visible strands on the beach-flat (bottom) are less than 6000 years old. The three levels of uplifted and tilted tabletop terraces are ancient beaches that developed from 120,000 to 80,000 years ago.

Plate 32 Paleoseismologists preparing drill cores near Wairoa. Examining sediments from drill cores is an excellent way to check for evidence of ancient sea-level changes. In this area, they might have been caused by subduction-thrust earthquakes.

Plate 33 View southeast across the Mohaka Fault to the junction of the Mohaka and Te Hoe rivers in Hawke's Bay. The Te Kooti Fault runs somewhere along the foot of the sandstone bluffs of Te Kooti's Lookout (left centre), but it is not considered active, and its trace is not visible at this site.

Plate 34 An active normal fault across the lonely Tutamoe plateau, north of Gisborne. The scarp is up to 8 metres high in places, and earthquakes can be expected from future ruptures. Few of the faults in this region are considered active, but it certainly had a turbulent past judging by the number of inactive faults (see figure 18).

Plate 35 Two parallel faults run across the northwest slopes of Tongariro. View southwards with Ngauruhoe and Ruapehu in the distance. Movement has occurred along these faults since the great Taupo eruption 1800 years ago, and the scarps are up to 10 metres high in places.

Plate 36 A strand of the Tumunui Fault Zone offsets volcanic materials in a road-cutting between Rotorua and Waiotapu. At this site, this normal fault has displaced pulses of debris from the 65,000-year-old Earthquake Flat eruption by 2 metres.

Plate 37 Regional view looking southwards toward the Tumunui Fault which offsets Tumunui Hill, a rhyolite lava dome. The 100-metre-high displacement has developed through numerous ruptures over the last 300,000 years or so. Beyond the Paeroa Range, the Ohaaki Geothermal Field is emitting plumes of steam, and Tauhara and Lake Taupo are at the top right.

Plate 38 High altitude view northeast to Mt Tarawera. The Paeroa Fault runs from bottom left and is marked by the bush-clad escarpment (plates 40 and 41). The small lake in the centre is a 700-year-old volcanic explosion crater, and its straightish right side marks the trend of the active Ngapouri Fault.

Plate 39 A trench excavation across a Paeroa Fault strand showing normal displacement of 2 metres. The very narrow white band at the top erupted from Mt Tarawera about 700 years ago, and the thick white band is 8500-year-old ash. Darker bands are soils that developed on ash, and were subsequently buried by later volcanic eruptions.

Plate 40 Looking northeast over the Te Kopia geothermal area on the Paeroa Fault, which curves into the distance at upper left. Note the tilt of the escarpment block of the Paeroa Range down towards the east.

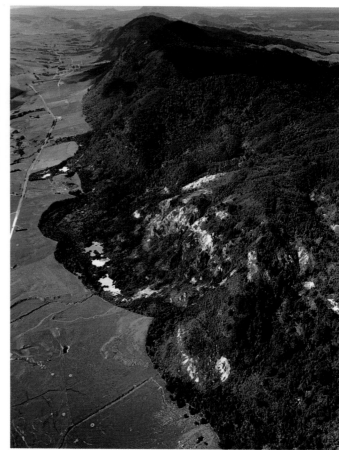

Plate 41 The northeast trending Paeroa Fault scarp is southeast of Rotorua. This 500-metre-high scarp formed through repeated rupturing along a normal fault over the last 400,000 years. While this may seem a lot of displacement, it only averages 1.25 mm each year.

Plate 42 The Horohoro escarpment (bottom left) marks the western margin of the active Taupo Volcanic Zone. It is the faulted edge of the Mamaku Plateau, which resulted from an eruption from Lake Rotorua when it was an active volcano about 210,000 years ago. The cliff segment is probably inactive, unlike other parts of the Horohoro Fault. Haparangi, the isolated round hill, is a lava dome. View northeast to Lake Rotorua.

Plates 43 and **44** Segments of the Paeroa Fault Zone displace 65,000-year-old volcanic breccia southeast of Rotorua near Waiotapu. Earthquake Flat Road (plate 43) is closed because of ground subsidence. These normal faults have many collapse structures, locally known as tomo (as in Waitomo), perhaps resulting from subterranean erosion along fault planes. View northeast over State Highway 5 (plate 44).

Plate 45 Trench excavation across the Horohoro Fault southwest of Rotorua. This normal fault segment has not ruptured in the last 2000 years. The thin band of cream tephra (upper right) erupted from the Rotorua volcano about 16,000 years ago. The tephra has been offset 4 metres since that time and is visible lower down the trench at left. This segment is considered active, but other parts of the Horohoro Fault are probably inactive.

Plate 46 View northwards over part of the 7-km-long surface rupture on the Edgecumbe Fault, which caused the damaging 1987 earthquake. The white patches close to the rupture are mixtures of water and sand that were liquefied and erupted because of the severe ground shaking.

Plate 47 This section of the Edgecumbe Fault, which ruptured up to the surface and caused the 1987 Edgecumbe Earthquake, has virtually no vertical offset. Other segments had up to 2 metres of vertical displacement after the rupture in 1987. The paleoseismologist is measuring depths of both the water and the fissure (not fishing).

Plate 48 Another fissure in water-rich sediments bisects the Hope River valley with a line of sag ponds at Glynn Wye, west of Hanmer Springs in North Canterbury. This part of the fault last moved in 1888 when it jumped 1.5 metres in a right-lateral movement. This rupture provided the first-ever scientific association of an earthquake with lateral movement along a geological fault (plates 8, 9 and 10).

Plate 49 Nelson City lies between the 250-million-year-old volcanic rocks of the Bryant Range (left) and sedimentary rocks younger than 5 million years that have been down-faulted to form the Moutere Depression (right). The city area also contains a succession of rocks deposited over the last 55 million years. Widespread faulting over the last 250 million years has disrupted older rocks and scarred the landscape. The currently active faults of the Waimea–Flaxmore Fault Zone run from left to distant centre.

Plate 50 The Waimea Fault at its onshore limit at Nile Head in D'Urville Island. View southwards, with 250+-million-year-old volcanic rocks west of the trace (arrowed) and younger, sedimentary rocks to the east. This part of the Waimea Fault is not considered to be active, but this area has a high seismic hazard because of ground shaking from earthquakes in Cook Strait or farther afield.

Plate 51 View northwards along the fault-bounded valleys southeast of Nelson. These include (left to right) the Waimea, Heslington, and Eighty-eight faults — all have some active segments.

Plate 52 View southwest towards Westport overlooking the complex scarp of the Kiwi Fault. This normal fault has offset 40-million-year-old Brunner Sandstone by up to 50 metres vertically.

Plate 53 View northwest towards Mt Frederick in Westland. The bush-clad ridge is the top of the Mt William Fault scarp, and running from upper left to top centre is the Kiwi Fault (plate 52). The Mt William Fault is probably still active. The bare patch in the foreground is a remnant of the Brunner Sandstone, a naturally infertile rock unit.

Plate 54 Damage from the Inangahua earthquake in 1968 affected nearly all services and caused extensive damage—chimneys were damaged or destroyed more than 150 km away. Parts of the railway embankment subsided because of the extreme ground shaking.

Plate 55 In 1968, many roads, pipes, and powerpoles were damaged and rearranged at Inangahua by ground-shaking. Subsidence, slumps, and major landslides, rather than surface ruptures, were the common results of the ground-shaking. The earthquake's intensity was locally felt at MMX, and MMIV in Dunedin and Napier.

Plate 56 The bare topography of Brunner Sandstone on the Stockton Plateau, north-east of Westport, is vertically offset about 200 metres by the Mt William Fault (plate 53). The sandstone overlies coal beds on both sides of the fault, but only the lower level has been mined.

Plate 57 Looking west to Lake Ohau behind the 100-metre-high scarp of a segment of the reverse-movement Ostler Fault. The scarp interrupts the outwash gravels from the last glaciation in the area.

Plate 58 Strike-slip movement on the reverse Lindis Fault, east of Lindis Pass, is clear from the offset drainage — note the sag pond. It was last active about 3500 years ago, and might move in 2-metre jumps. This may not bode well for the power pylons and the road that cross the fault trace at the top left of this photograph.

Plate 59 The Ostler Fault west of Lake Benmore shows two of the many surface ruptures in this reverse fault zone. Progressive uplift has resulted from repeated earth-quaking ruptures — the front scarp is 5 to 6 metres high, and the back one is about 100 m high. Landslides obscure the most recent traces of the uplifted section to the left.

Plate 60 View northwards along another part of the Ostler Fault; Lake Pukaki is to the right, and Mt Cook is in the distance. The trace disrupts the topography of Jurassic greywacke. The scarp faces uphill which is relatively common in reverse faults, although it can occur with other faults depending on the dip of the fault plane.

Plate 61 View south along the Livingstone Fault from Four Brothers Pass above the Olivine River in northwest Otago. The fault separates 250+-million-year-old volcanic rocks and serpentine (right) from younger schist rocks on the left. The different rock types are most clearly shown on the skyline, where the red weathered serpentine of Fiery Peak butts against the snowy tops of the schist. All are on the Pacific Plate. The Livingstone Fault is not considered currently active.

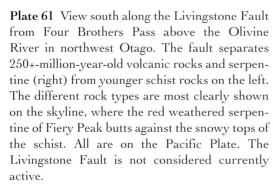

Plate 62 View southwest along strands of the Moonlight Fault and the Von River valley, southwest of Lake Wakatipu. One strand runs across the slope at centre left, and another follows the dark shadowy gully at lower right. The Moonlight Fault splits again with branches on either side of Bald Hill in the distance — some strands are active. The Thomson Mountains (right) are underlain by 250+-million-year-old sandstone, and the valley floor is glacial material deposited during the last two million years.

Plate 63 Looking northeast from the Eyre Mountains along the Moonlight Fault, where it crosses Lake Wakatipu. Roughly parallel strands of the fault zone follow the dark gully (left) and through the notched spur at centre right. The main fault leaves the lake at Bob's Cove (by the pale paddock over the lake) and follows the valley running from there into the distant centre skyline. Small active faults associated with the Moonlight Fault cut the low lakeside hills (bottom).

Plate 64 View southwards over Lake Roxburgh, its dam, and the lower Clutha River, with the Blue Mountains in the distance. The East Roxburgh Fault runs from the lower left. The Teviot Fault (arrowed from lower right) crosses the river twice and roughly parallels the Old Man Fault (arrowed mid-right). All these reverse faults are possibly active, but there is a long recurrence interval between ruptures.

Plate 65 The Dunstan Fault extends along the shadowed Dairy Creek gully (lower right) and crosses the Clutha River about 700 metres upstream from the Clyde Dam. On the far side of the river, the curving fault structure continues as the Cairnmuir Fault, which offsets the light-coloured plateau from the darker Cairnmuir Mountains. View southwest, with another strand of the Dunstan Fault offsetting the plateau from the riverside paddocks opposite Clyde township.

Plate 66 This southern extension to the Old Man Fault has probably been active within the last 500,000 years, but not recently. View northwards across Ettrick and the Clutha River, 15 km downstream from the Roxburgh Dam.

Plate 67 The Blue Mountain Fault along the foot of the Blue Mountain in Otago is considered to be active. It is a reverse fault with a steeply dipping fault plane. View north over Tapanui with the Old Man Range in the distance at upper left.

Plate 68 The rocky coastline at Taieri Mouth results from uplift along the Akatore Fault. The trace of this reverse fault crosses the road at the bend (foreground) and passes out to sea to the left of the coastal rocks and the uplifted Taieri Island. The ridges parallel to the shore north of Taieri Mouth are not fault traces, but former shorelines that probably resulted from a mixture of sea-level changes and tectonic movement. View northeast towards Dunedin.

Plate 69 The Akatore Fault, south of Dunedin, splits a coastal block of 150-million-year-old schist. The seaward sliver has been uplifted in reverse fault movements, creating the depression across the bottom of the photo. On the downside of a 3-metre-high fault, trace (arrowed) is conglomerate rock that was deposited about 75-million-years ago when the area was coastal swamp. The earth-quaking rupture that created this scarp occurred about 1500 years ago, temporarily damming Nobles Stream, which has since managed to cut through the raised block and reach the coast.

Plate 70 View southwest over the upper Taieri River towards the fault-bound Rough Ridge, some 15 km southwest of Ranfurly in Central Otago. The Poolburn reservoir is at top right. Meandering along for millions of years, the upper Taieri River has countless abandoned channels, loops, oxbow lakes, and curving banks. The Rough Ridge Fault offsets the 150+-million-year-old schists of Rough Ridge, which have been uplifted and had 150 million years of overlying rock eroded, from young glacial and river gravels in the valley.

Plate 71 The glamour of geology is not restricted to tramping around in the bush or choppering to distant peaks and hammering at mountain tops while the chopper parks on one skid. For absolutely no extra qualification, you can play in knee-deep mud and unravel the rock and rupture history of geological faults. Paleoseismologists David Heron, Peter Wood and Russ van Dissen from the Institute of Geological and Nuclear Sciences are deep in their work.

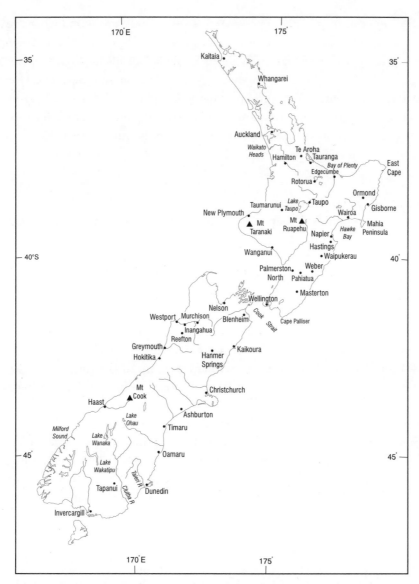

Figure 10 Locations relevant to discussions of New Zealand's geological faults that do not necessarily appear in other maps.

Imagine a region with a deformation rate that averages 30 mm per year, and also that its last big earthquake occurred exactly 100 years ago. If the fault slip at that time was 3 metres, one would sincerely hope that the locals would have considered earthquake effects in their building codes, engineering designs, and Civil Defence procedures.

Information from earth-deformation studies and fault monitoring provides the base for planning and land-use decisions. The Resource Management Act requires local and regional councils to know about all geological hazards in their areas, so that plans can be made to protect communities. The effects of hazards are minimised through building codes, planning consents, engineering guidelines, and public information. To make these plans realistic, details on the frequency and location of quakes, and the ongoing rates of earth deformation, need to be regularly updated.

National deformation

If measuring earth deformation were compared to skinning a cat (with a view to something unmentionable), its only point of similarity would be the number of methods available. Earthquakes provide information about the location and amount of deformation energy that is released in a single event. Geological faults provide a direction, areal extent, and history for releases of this deformation energy. Clever surveying techniques involving satellites in a Global Positioning System (GPS) can measure the amount of deformation that is currently building up that might be released in a major earthquake.

GPS surveying is accurate to millimetres — up to 100 times more accurate than conventional surveying over 10 to 50 km. Accordingly, movements that would take 100 years to detect by standard methods can be detected by GPS surveys done a year or two apart. Concrete monuments similar to trig stations are set up in areas of active deformation, and the angles, distances, and height differences between monuments are measured with stunning precision over huge distances — for example, between the Chatham Islands and Australia. Regular measurements from 260 GPS stations show that nearly all New Zealand is on the move. Such geoscience surveying is called geodesy; this is the science that determines the size and shape of the earth, and precisely locates points on its surface.

Local geodetic geologists plot deformation information on maps to show the velocity at which any point in New Zealand is moving, relative to points within the interior of the Australian Plate (figure 11). These velocities can be as high as 40 mm per year. (Millimetres-per-year is a great way to work in geological time. Because there are a million millimetres in a kilometre, 40 mm per year equals 40 km every million years.) In the southern North Island there is little change in velocity on either side of the trench, which means that much of the Pacific Plate motion transmits into the Australian Plate causing it to squash and deform throughout the region. This deformation is certain to be released in major earthquakes, some of which will rupture the plate interface with shattering results.

Figure 11 shows a big change in velocity across the Hikurangi Trough off Hawke's Bay and Gisborne. Deformation on the Australian Plate is in a different direction and occurs at a different rate. This indicates that the motion of the Pacific Plate is not being transmitted into the overlying Australian Plate and, therefore, that the Pacific Plate is subducting smoothly and does not cause much deformation in the overlying plate. Relatively speaking, of course.

Where velocity changes only a small amount between nearby points, not much deformation is occurring — and vice versa — big changes in direction

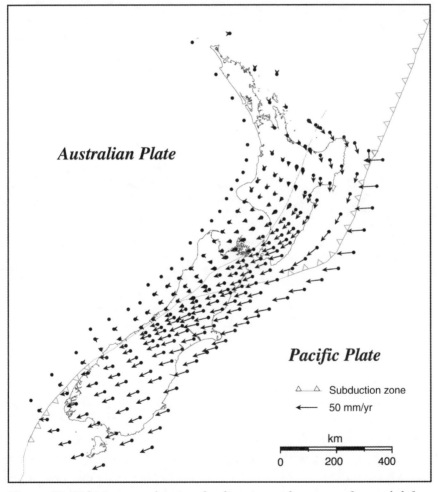

Figure 11 Velocity map showing the direction and amount of crustal deformation in different parts of New Zealand. The dots are reference points, the arrows show the direction of movement, and the length of the arrow indicates the rate of movement. The western edge of the Axial Tectonic Belt is drawn through the North Island.

Figure 12 Time-averaged rates of crustal deformation measured between 1996 and 1999. The light lines are geological faults, the circles are geodetic survey monuments, and the arrow lengths indicate the amount of movement that has taken place.

The western coastal area is remarkable for its relative stability, while the whole region east of the Alpine Fault is moving at rates of up to 30 mm per year. The progressive change from small velocities near Nelson to large ones near Kaikoura shows that the crust is not just moving, but also changing shape (deforming) pervasively throughout the region. Generally, ruptures in the upper crust occur along existing paths of weakness, in spite of the deformation during the interval between earthquakes being so regionally widespread.

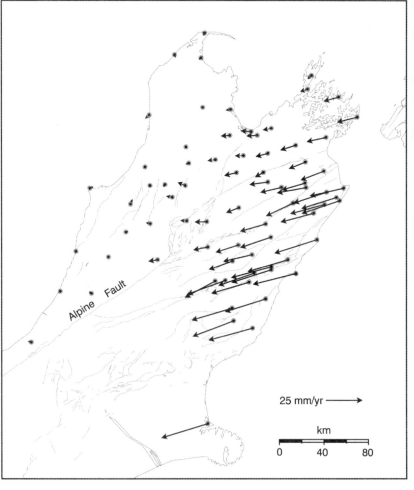

or velocity within the same neighbourhood indicate large movements and much deformation.

The deformation rates under the Southern Alps are the highest in the country. This implies a big build-up of energy that will eventually be released in massive earthquakes. However, there is another possible explanation.

The local style of oblique plate convergence causes the rapid uplift of the Alps, and consequently the rock temperatures beneath the Alps are much warmer than normal. These raised temperatures may allow the rocks to deform and dissipate energy by ductile flow, rather than snap and rupture as a brittle material. Such thermal interference means that some of the deformation measured geodetically at the surface may result from ongoing steady processes.

If such steady processes are occurring, the size of the earthquakes could be smaller than generally anticipated, or the intervals between earthquakes could be longer. The jury is still out on the preferred explanation.

CONFESS OUR FAULTS

New Zealand has more than 150 geological faults that are known to be active, and many of them twitch repeatedly; about 200 earthquakes a year are big enough to be felt. Earthquakes that damage buildings are mostly greater than magnitude 6, and there is generally only one of these a year. A magnitude 7

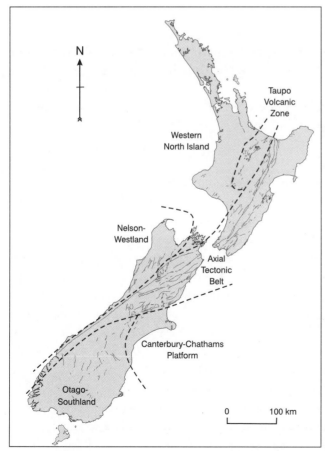

Figure 13 New Zealand's active tectonic provinces and the main geological faults that have been active during the last 100,000 years. The fault traces preserve a geological record of the location and magnitude of large shallow earthquakes. These usually need a magnitude greater than 6.5 to rupture the ground surface in New Zealand conditions.

The Taupo Volcanic Zone has mostly normal faults, and the North Island part of the Axial Tectonic Belt is a zone of right-lateral strike-slip faults, with a strip of reverse faults along the east coast. The Axial Tectonic Belt in the South Island deforms as a result of oblique stress, and its faults have both strike-slip and dip-slip movements, but strike-slip movements dominate the deformation pattern.

Compressive forces have a marginal lead over lateral shearing in the rest of the South Island.

earthquake occurs about once every ten years and, on average, a magnitude 8 happens once a century. Shallow crustal earthquakes cause more damage than quakes of the same magnitude, but with deeper focal depths. Unfortunately, earthquakes sometime occur in clusters, so the averaging procedure that indicates that a magnitude 7 comes once a decade really only means that within a hundred years there are likely to be about ten magnitude 7 quakes.

New Zealand can be divided into active tectonic provinces according to the style and speed of tectonic deformation and its consequent earthquakes (figure 13). The provinces vary in the depths of their earthquakes, as well as the amounts of deformation and the lengths of time between major quakes. Variation within each province is also the rule, rather than the exception.

Axial Tectonic Belt

The Axial Tectonic Belt is the busiest of New Zealand's active tectonic provinces. It is about 1000 km long and extends through the eastern North Island, Marlborough, North Canterbury, and some of Westland and Fiordland. Most of the country's deformation occurs within this belt, and deformation hazards are about ten times greater here than elsewhere. In the South Island, the Axial Tectonic Belt is bounded by the Alpine Fault, the onshore part of the boundary between the Pacific and Australian plates. In the North Island, it includes the dramatic Wellington and Wairarapa faults, and has produced the infamous east coast earthquakes.

South Island

Running from Milford Sound to Blenheim, the 650-km-long Alpine Fault is a right-lateral, strike-slip fault with different segments that behave in different ways. In its southernmost part, it seems purely strike-slip with a very steeply dipping fault plane (see back cover photograph). Central segments of the Alpine Fault have significant dip-slip movement on a moderately sloping plane because of compressive forces. The northern segments produce mostly strike-slip movement, but at slower rates. Deformation from this plate-boundary movement extends back into the Pacific Plate and uplifts the Southern Alps. A major fault system with considerable internal deformation parallels the Alpine Fault for 60 km in the Pacific crust along the eastern side of the Alps. This Main Divide Fault Zone comprises numerous reverse faults that dip towards the Alpine Fault, and their traces add to the crumpled and jagged look of the Alps.

Earthquakes from central and southern Alpine Fault segments are generally very shallow, mainly because there is no subducting plate to bend, creak and rupture at great depths. A high subterranean heatflow associated with the rapid uplift of the deep, warmer rocks that create the Southern Alps also limits the region's potential for deep earthquakes. Accelerating uplift and erosion over the last 5 million years, with modern rates up to 10 mm per year, have created a surface temperature gradient of about 60°C per km. This means that only quite shallow rocks will snap in a brittle rupture, whereas rocks below about 10 km will deform by ductile flow.

The Alpine Fault has given rise to four earthquakes approaching magnitude 8 in the last 900 years. The time-averaged displacement of rock on one side relative to the other is about 37 mm per year, and major quakes have resulted from typical 'jumps' some 6 to 8 metres horizontally and 1 to 2 metres vertically. The ability of the area to accommodate vast amounts of stress (and build up vast amounts of energy that can be released in one big hit), and its tendency to rupture at shallow depths, have the potential for a profound impact on the landscape. Massive landslides, rockfalls, and avalanches may dam rivers and streams. Major changes to river flows and large waves in lakes are expected and some types of soil will behave like a liquid, causing structures to sink, tilt, or topple. Roads, bridges, powerpoles, and services will be severely rearranged. If the faulting were centrally located on the Alpine Fault (figure 14), such effects could extend from Reefton to Haast, and some infrastructure may not be restored for years.

In the far south of the Alpine Fault, the fault plane is almost vertical (see back cover photograph) and the oblique convergent stress of the two plates moving together is taken up by other geological structures in Fiordland and western Southland. Farther north, the Alpine Fault plane accommodates most of the plate motion along a moderately east-dipping reverse fault so there is both horizontal and vertical movement on the central part of the fault plane.

Pieces of the fault have segmented traces that partly overlap each other, although the segments strike in the same general direction. Just north of the Haast River, the segments are 200 to 300 metres long with scarps between 5 to 10 metres high. One small creek suddenly hangs a right turn for nearly 100 metres along the foot of the scarp before it turns seawards. The rate of horizontal offset for the last 4000 years averages out at 25 mm per year and the vertical offset is nearly 3 mm per year.

In 1998, multidisciplinary research concluded that big quakes occur on the Alpine Fault every 100 to 300 years. The two most recent earthquakes on the fault are both estimated at magnitude 8. They are dated to AD 1720 and 1620. Two previous magnitude 8 quakes on the Alpine Fault occurred about AD 1450 and 1100. So, if this sequence continues, a big one on the central part of the Alpine Fault is due anytime now. It will release about 30 times more energy than the 1968 Inangahua quake. Ground-shaking intensities throughout the

Figure 14 Expected ground-shaking intensities on the Modified Mercalli Scale for an Alpine Fault rupture that releases its stored energy by strike- and dip-slip movements. Parts of the fault in the MM8 area will rupture to the surface. The ground may be offset by 8 metres sideways and 1 to 2 metres vertically.

This model is based on earthquake ruptures from the historical catalogue, which does not include a central Alpine Fault earthquake because there hasn't been one. The isoseismal contours for MM7 and greater will probably be more elliptical — covering a longer but narrower area — than is shown here. The position of the epicentre is arbitrary.

South Island will be stronger and longer lasting than any jolts ever recorded in the area. Clearly, the Alpine Fault is a significant seismic hazard for the entire South Island ('hazard' is the probability of damage occurring).

When the next big one happens, frighteningly recognisable by perhaps a minute or more of shaking, it is a signal for West Coasters to move quickly, very quickly, away from rivers and lakes. This is basic Safety First, but great care must be taken to pick higher ground that is not threatened by the rock-falls and avalanches that are bound to happen near the epicentre. Just in case any North Islanders are tempted to complacency or smugness, it is calculated that a severe Alpine Fault earthquake will waken sleepers, dislodge ornaments and crockery, and may crack some windows in North Island areas including New Plymouth, Palmerston North and, of course, Wellington (figure 14).

Several very important subparallel strike-slip faults across North Canterbury and Marlborough define a 100- by 200-km zone that transfers deformation across the northern South Island between the Alpine Fault and Hikurangi Trough. It includes the Kakapo, Hope, Clarence, and Awatere faults, and the northern part of the Alpine Fault, known as the Wairau Fault. Because the Australian and Pacific plates converge obliquely, the faults are mainly strike-slip, with the sense of movement for rocks on the opposite side of the fault being to your right, regardless of which side you are standing on.

The ongoing uplift of the Southern Alps, however, illustrates the increasing regional compression towards the south because the Alpine Fault strikes at a more oblique angle to the direction of the Pacific Plate's movement (figure 5).

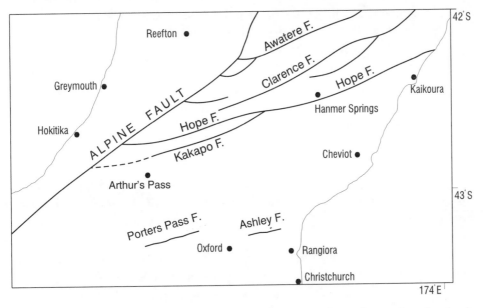

Figure 15 Major active faults in the South Island transform the motion that leads from subduction off the coast of the North Island to oblique lateral shearing along the Alpine Fault.

The Wairau section of the Alpine Fault (plates 4 and 5) carried most of the movement until the southward propagation of the Hikurangi subduction zone instigated the formation of the Marlborough faults about 10 million years ago. Today the Hope Fault accommodates much of the plate boundary deformation and appears to host most of the seismic activity. Fifteen moderate to large earthquakes have occurred in the Marlborough Fault Zone since historical records began. The roughly parallel Clarence and Awatere faults (plates 6 and 7) are also active areas of deformation. None of these faults has been reliably traced offshore or across Cook Strait.

In 1888, a rupture on the Hope Fault at Glynn Wye, west of Hanmer Springs, caused a shallow earthquake (plate 48). It offset fences and farm tracks by 2.6 metres of right-lateral movement, and it produced 30 km of surface rupture, but there was no significant vertical displacement. The quake's magnitude is estimated at 7.3, and the rupture provided a world-first in relating strike-slip displacement to an earthquake. Although the quake was centred some 100 km from Christchurch, it damaged the Cathedral spire, which copped quake-induced damage several times during the nineteenth century.

The average movement along the Hope Fault is 15 to 25 mm per year, resulting from displacement with a return period at any one place of 80 to 200 years. Its typical earth-quaking rupture is a horizontal offset of about 2 metres. Segments of the Hope Fault may rupture with less provocation in terms of energy build-up, than the Alpine Fault, and at some time within the next few decades (plates 8 to 10).

Strike-slip movement on the Kakapo Fault caused a magnitude 7 earthquake at Arthur's Pass in 1929 (figure 15). The immediate area was sparsely settled, so community damage was not extensive, but the quake was felt throughout the South Island and north to Taranaki. The 1994 Arthur's Pass earthquake, which occurred on a small neighbouring fault plane, was the largest in the region since the 1929 effort. This shallow quake, magnitude 6.7, originated about 5 km down on a reverse fault plane. It created some 70 landslides and the state highway was blocked for a week. The Earthquake Commission received more than $5 million in damage claims, mostly from the Christchurch area, 120 km away from the epicentre.

The major Marlborough earthquake in 1848 was probably less than 10 km deep under the lower Awatere Valley (plate 6) and it is estimated at magnitude 7.5. Its fault rupture was 105 km long, with a strike-slip displacement of about 6 metres to the right. More than 90 aftershocks were reported over the next two weeks, mostly by people in Wellington, where many brick buildings were damaged. The largest of the aftershocks 'destroyed all the brick stores at Te Aro and rent the Native Hospital in pieces. It also split the brick barrack at the Kaiwarra end of the town and the jail at Mount Cook,' according to one contemporary account. Fortunately, many of the pioneers decided to rebuild in wood, so tragedy was largely avoided when, seven years later, an even bigger quake occurred on the Wairarapa Fault.

Beneath Marlborough the plates appear to be permanently locked together, and no large subduction thrusts, creating subduction-thrust earthquakes, are expected while the plates are locked. The coupling strength is the indirect result of the crustal thickness, some 15 km, of the Pacific Plate. North of Gisborne, the subducting crust is 10 km thick and its coupling is weak. These thicknesses are much greater than most deep-sea trenches have to cope with (globally, oceanic crust averages nearly 6 km). They probably give rise to the coastal ranges because the overlying plate is forced upwards to accommodate the efforts of subducting thick and buoyant crust. The intense deformation in Marlborough and North Canterbury, including the rapid uplift of the Inland and Seaward Kaikoura ranges, accounts for nearly all the relative plate movement in this region. The locked interface produces strong earthquakes in the overlying crust.

North Island

From Wellington north to the Manawatu Gorge, the subducting and overlying plates are strongly coupled together for a down-dip distance of 70 km, and subduction-thrust earthquakes on the interface are expected to create magnitude 8 earthquakes. If the entire subducting interface from Wellington to East Cape ruptured, research suggests that a magnitude 8.3 quake would occur.

The size and strength of the coupled zone seems to decrease to the northeast, from permanently locked under Marlborough, strong under Wellington, moderate under Hawke's Bay, and weak under East Cape. This means that not as much energy is stored up before the subducting plate thrusts downwards in the northern areas. A subduction-thrust earthquake on the boundary interface north of Tolaga Bay might create an earthquake of about magnitude 6.9.

Shallow earthquakes that are recorded and located in the Wellington region are scattered and do not correlate well with the known fault traces (figure 16). However, in the past, large quakes have occurred — on the Wairarapa Fault in 1855 and on the Wellington Fault about 350 to 500 years ago. Although little seismic activity is currently associated with these faults, they will eventually rupture again causing magnitude 7+ quakes.

The magnitude 8+ Wairarapa earthquake in 1855 occurred on the Wairarapa Fault (plates 21 to 23), which comes ashore from Cook Strait east of Cape Turakirae. It runs northeast for at least 140 km and defines the eastern edge of the Rimutaka and Tararua ranges. With its focus less than 15 km deep, the 1855 quake was felt over the whole country and at least five people died as a result of it. Its intensity at Wellington was MMX.

The 1855 movement of the Wairarapa Fault created the greatest amount of earth deformation and surface rupturing associated with any earthquake then known, and it is still the most extreme since records began. There was severe ground-shaking, extensive faulting, landslides, and regional uplift. While the Wellington region was most affected, much damage also occurred at Wanganui and Kaikoura. Landslides occurred around the Rimutaka Range and along the Kaikoura coast, and slump cracks and sand craters appeared in flat parts of the Manawatu area.

Some 5000 square kilometres west of the Wairarapa Fault were raised and tilted. The greatest vertical offset, 6 metres, was on the Wairarapa coast at

Figure 16 Active faults and earthquakes greater than magnitude 3 within the top 40 km under the Wellington region, 1990 to 1993. The Pacific Plate starts subducting about 120 km east of the Wairarapa coast. It is already 15 km deep below Cape Palliser at the southeast point of the North Island, and about 25 km deep beneath Wellington. Nearly all quakes shown are in the Australian crust. The cluster in the southeast originates on the interface between the Pacific and Australian plates.

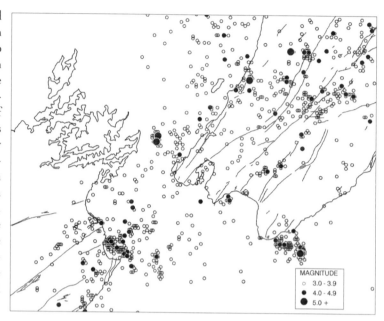

Turakirae Head (plate 20) and this uplift decreased northwest across the Wellington Peninsula to almost nothing at Paekakariki on the far coast (plate 14). The strip of land on which the Hutt motorway is built was uplifted and emerged from the harbour. The Wairarapa Fault ruptured up to the surface for about 140 km, with a recently calculated horizontal movement of at least 9 metres along a 72-km stretch of the surface rupture, as well as the vertical movement.

Water slopped back and forth across Wellington Harbour for eight to twelve hours, and seiches were reported in rivers, lakes, and harbours from Waikato to Otago. Two or three aftershocks a day continued for six weeks. This must have been terrifying for the settlers — at least five of the hundreds of aftershocks were greater than magnitude 6.5. Surface displacement up to 12 metres is expected to accompany a future major quake on the Wairarapa Fault.

Recent shallow quakes in this region are probably associated with small movements on minor faults that have not ruptured up to the surface. Earthquakes up to magnitude 6.5 can occur at any time, but they are unlikely to rupture the surface. However, other faults may rupture to the surface causing major earthquakes, and the land on either side of the Wellington, Ohariu, and Shepherds Gully fault traces may shift 3 to 5 metres (figure 17). The Ohariu Fault runs from Cook Strait to Waikanae and is capable of rupturing to produce earthquakes with magnitudes up to 7.6, but its recurrence interval is estimated at once every 1500 to 5000 years which puts it rather down the hazard-priority list (plates 17 to 19).

The biggest seismic hazard for Wellington City is the probability of a major rupture on the Wellington Fault (plates 11 to 16). This runs from Cook Strait, through the Karori reservoirs, and along the northwest side of the harbour and the western side of the Hutt Valley (plates 13 and 14). This hazard is greatest because it runs close to large population centres, and it seems to move more frequently than other faults in the region. It will also be relatively shallow because it will occur in the brittle crust. Accordingly, thousands of people could live within 10 km of the quake's focus. Areas on recently deposited, water-saturated, soft sediment will shake two to three times longer than nearby hard rock or compacted gravel sites.

Major ruptures on the Wellington Fault recur about every 600 years. The time 'envelope' for a magnitude 7.5 quake is once every 500 to 770 years. Displacement on the Wellington Fault during the last five major earthquakes averages about 4 metres horizontally and up to 1 metre vertically for each event. The last big one ruptured the Wellington Fault between 350 and 500 years ago, and the probability of another large earthquake hitting Wellington within the next 30 years is about 12 percent. This is a one-in-eight chance of a very big one within 30 years (better than Lotto!). Subduction-thrust earthquakes are much less frequent and some seismic modelling research suggests that they possibly average once every 800 to 900 years. Trouble is, there are few clues as to when the last one happened.

The Wellington to Hawke's Bay stretch of the Axial Tectonic Belt is one of the busiest deformation areas because the force of the subducting Pacific Plate beneath it crumples the crust. The interface coupling between the subducting Pacific and overlying Australian plates at the southern end of the Hikurangi

Table 2 Major faults within the Wellington area and their earthquake potential.
*Estimates regarding subduction-thrust earthquakes come from seismic modelling, not observations, and the measures are approximate.

Faults	Years since last major quake	Recurrence interval in years	Fault offset in metres	Estimated magnitude
Wairapa	145	1160-1880	9.0-13.5	8.0-8.3
Wellington	340-490	500-770	3.7-4.7	7.6±0.3
Ohariu	1110-1190	1500-5000	3.0-5.0	7.6±0.3
Shepherds Gully	>1200	2500-5000	3.5-4.0	7.6±0.3
Wairau/Alpine	>800	1000-2300	5.0-7.0	7.6±0.3
Subduction thrust*	>160	~875	~4.2	8.0

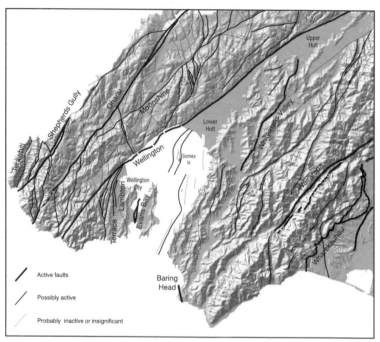

Figure 17 The Wellington region has been deforming and producing geological faults because of various tectonic regimes over the last 130 million years.

The Whitemans Valley Fault is a newly discovered active reverse fault with a total scarp height of 8 to 9 metres. Although its contribution to the region's seismic hazard is small, it does signal the probability of similar undiscovered faults in rugged topography.

Trough is strong, and the overlying crust has obligingly deformed to account for all the relative plate movement in the last 100 years. Along the coast, and offshore from it, the stress is mainly compressive. This has uplifted the coastal ranges, and the faults have a reverse movement. Nearly all fault traces parallel the subduction zone, and eight of the nineteen onshore earthquakes since 1840 that have magnitudes greater than 6.5 are in the Wellington to Hawke's Bay stretch (plates 25, 26 and 27).

The eastern North Island also hosts the nastiest regional cluster of large quakes ever recorded in New Zealand: 1931 Napier, 1932 Wairoa, 1934 Pahiatua, 1938 Hawke's Bay, and two scary earthquakes just five weeks apart near Masterton in 1942. These two magnitude 7+ earthquakes shook the Wairarapa and caused so much damage to old buildings and structures that the government was inspired to set up the Earthquake and War Damage Commission to help people rebuild after disasters. A narrow belt of severe ground surface disruption extended over 60 km near Masterton, and the first quake was felt from Auckland to Dunedin. Damage to private and public buildings was extensive in Wellington and the Wellington City Council organised repairs to local household chimneys — a large proportion of the estimated 20,000 chimneys damaged by the earthquake.

The people of southern Hawke's Bay must have felt uneasy during 1990 when a magnitude 6.1 quake in February was followed by a 6.2 quake in May and a 5.5 quake in August. Like the 1942 Masterton earthquakes, the epicentres of the earthquakes at Weber were very close to each other, but they were focused at different depths, and were prompted by different local stresses. None was accompanied by surface rupture, and data on the fault displacement comes from seismic analyses.

The first occurred on a steeply dipping normal fault within the subducting Pacific Plate as it bent and was pulled downwards by its own weight and convection processes. We know that the fault was within the subducting plate and not a case of subduction-thrust, because the interface between the two plates is about 20 km below Weber, whereas the earthquake originated at 31 km. The second earthquake occurred 17 km down on a shallow reverse fault in the crust of the overlying Australian Plate. The smaller third quake was again on a normal fault within the subducting plate, as was a fourth in 1992.

Farther to the west, the massive Mohaka and Ruahine faults (northern extensions of the Wellington Fault) have sinuous traces more than 400 km long that roughly parallel the subduction zone (plates 24, 28 and 33). They are both strike-slip faults with fault planes that dip between 60° and 90° in different segments. They show nearly 300 metres of displacement over the last three

Figure 18 The potential of fault ruptures within the crust of a subducting plate to create seismic hazards for communities on the overlying plate is becoming more apparent as research continues into the eastern North Island's regional geology, tectonic structures and earthquakes.

No quakes larger than magnitude 6 have occurred within 40 km of the Mahia Peninsula (plate 31) since historic records began, but if the whole length of the local fault ruptures in a single event, a magnitude 7.5 quake would be expected.

Future large crustal earthquakes associated with the subducting plate could lift 1500 square kilometres by up to 5 metres.

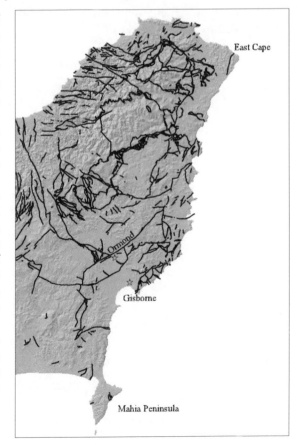

million years, and their hazard is similar to that of the Wellington Fault.

At many localities farther up the east coast, there are sequences of beach terraces with different levels of estuary and tidal deposits. These raised beaches were uplifted when large earthquakes ruptured along reverse faults in the crust of the overlying plate. The dreadful 1931 Napier earthquake ruptured enough rock in a reverse and strike-slip movement to suddenly and permnently raise the local coast by about 3 metres in just seconds. Some of the raised-beach sequences have been dated, and provide an excellent record of the magnitude and timing of past earthquakes. These indicate the expected intervals between future quakes.

In 1993, the magnitude 6.3 Ormond earthquake near Gisborne prompted the immediate placement of four temporary seismographs to supplement the National Seismograph Network. This was an effort to track the aftershock pattern, integrate the rates and strengths of ground shaking, and to examine the segmentation and style of the faulting in detail.

The boundary between the two plates is about 22 km below Ormond and, as the rupture began 37 km down, it must have been within the subducting Pacific Plate (figure 18). Shaking intensities reached MMVIII locally, with liquefaction, ground cracking, and landslides, and shaking was widely felt in the eastern North Island. The aftershock pattern was different in the subducting crust to that in the subducting lithosphere. This reflects the temperature change to warmer, less brittle rock, which can absorb greater stress without rupturing, in the lithosphere. The smaller proportion of lithosphere aftershocks may also show that the fault plane was relatively smooth, rupturing cleanly at the first go.

An important finding from the dense array of seismometers around Ormond is that the two tectonic plates are not strongly coupled in the subduction zone offshore from the Gisborne area, but move past each other relatively smoothly. This is the same conclusion that is reached through geodetic measurements of crustal deformation.

The whole East Cape region is rotating clockwise at about 4° every million years in what seems to be a natural consequence of the weak coupling between the plates. This clockwise rotation creates extension stress in the Taupo Volcanic Zone, and helps pull it apart.

Taupo Volcanic Zone

The Taupo Volcanic Zone is a narrow north-to-south basin from White Island and the Bay of Plenty in the north to Mt Ruapehu in the south (figures 13 and 19; plates 29 and 35 to 47). It has developed within the last 2 million years and currently has only 8 to 10 km of brittle crust, which is getting thinner because of active extensional stresses that cause stretching. The East Cape is certainly becoming more distant from the Coromandel Peninsula, and research indicates that the zone is widening at an average rate of 8 to 10 mm per year.

Geoscientists are studying whether all this deformation will be released in future earthquakes. The deformation is distributed across many short faults that strike northeast and accommodate vertical movements associated with the stretching and extension of the crust in this area. The earthquake pattern reflects this deformation with a wedge of shallow quakes trending northeast from Ruapehu, and marking the eastern edge of the zone — just in case you missed the row of volcanoes.

Heat flow in the upper crust is thirteen times greater than normal, and the Taupo Volcanic Zone has more than twenty geothermal systems, some of which provide steam for generating electricity. The zone is characterised by geothermal springs, volcanoes, numerous normal faults, and many small shallow quakes that often occur in earthquake swarms. Averaged over about 400,000 years, rates of movement along faults in the north of this region are about 7 mm per year. However, large earthquakes such as the magnitude 6.3 at Edgecumbe in 1987, can kick in a millennium's worth of movement in a matter of seconds (plates 46, 47 and front cover photograph).

The 1987 Edgecumbe earthquake contributed 1.3 metres of horizontal extension and the Rangitaiki Plains dropped 2 metres on the western side of the fault trace, decreasing the effectiveness of the area's drainage. The rupture began nearly 10 km down, travelled to the surface, and produced at least eleven surface ruptures over an area of 16 km by 10 km. They are all normal faults and most were associated with existing faults, ground fissures, and surface warping. The largest rupture was a metre wide and snaked northeast for about 7 km (plate 46).

This magnitude 6.3 quake caused extensive damage in the Bay of Plenty, and was felt in Hamilton, Taupo, Napier, and Gisborne. Intensities of MMIX were felt near the epicentre. Severe damage to structures was confined to within 20 km of the epicentre, which is typical of moderate magnitude, shallow earthquakes. Many aftershocks, three over magnitude 5, were recorded. A foreshock of magnitude 4.9 occurred just seven minutes before the main shock, and was largely responsible for the evacuation of buildings, some of which were badly damaged in the main shock. Damage has been estimated at $300 million.

More than 80 percent of the recorded earthquakes in the Taupo Volcanic Zone originate in the top 6 km of the earth's crust. Many scientists consider that only the top 6 km are sufficiently brittle to host earthquakes in this zone — below that depth the crust deforms in a ductile manner because of the high heat flow within the rocks.

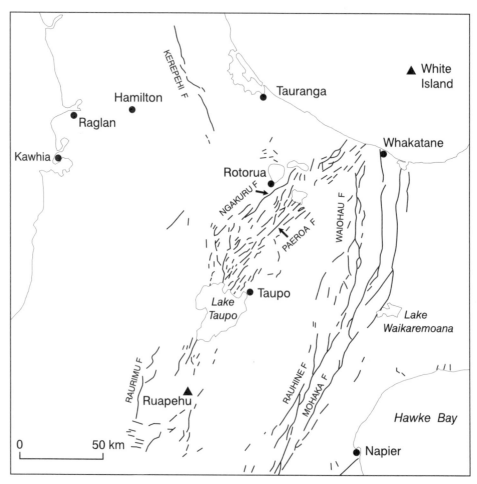

Figure 19 Geological faults of the Taupo Volcanic Zone — the strip from Ruapehu to White Island — and the northern extension of the Wellington regional faults. The Taupo Volcanic Zone is internationally famous because of its active volcanoes, crustal extension and geothermal activity, and close proximity to a subduction zone.

The destruction caused by earthquakes diminishes with distance from the quake's origin, regardless of whether it is horizontal distance from the epicentre, or oblique distance from the focus. Because its earthquakes are so shallow, the Taupo Volcanic Zone is much more likely to be severely rattled by a magnitude 5 quake than, for example, a Wanganui district earthquake directly above the focus of magnitude 5. Earthquake swarms, sequences of smallish quakes that are clustered in time and space but are not associated with an identifiable mainshock, and episodes of gentle subsidence are quite common (plates 43 and 44). However, they are variable with respect to the amount of slip on a fault and the intervals between events that rupture the surface.

Nelson–Westland

The Nelson–Westland tectonic province north and west of the Alpine Fault is the only part of the South Island on the Australian Plate. It contains numerous sets of reverse faults, with time-averaged movements of less than 1 mm per year. Historical records in this region over the last 150 years tell of more frequent earthquakes than are estimated from field geology.

Field evidence such as fault offsets in trenches and displaced streams indicate that the high historical numbers are unusual given the averaged long-term fault offsets and the averaged length of time between major events within the province. Five clearly active faults in the Waimea–Flaxmore Fault Zone have significant surface ruptures, presumably associated with shallow crustal earthquakes that occurred during the last 125,000 years (plates 49 to 51).

The fatal 1929 Murchison earthquake moved a segment of the White Creek Fault some 4.5 metres vertically and 2+ metres horizontally. The surface rupture could only be traced for 8 km, but given the quake's 7.8 magnitude, the area of the rupture plane must have been considerable. Seventeen people died, mostly in earthquake-generated landslides. The quake's focus was about 9 km below the surface and the ground shaking was felt all over New Zealand. Fortunately, the area was sparsely populated, because the maximum intensity was MMX, enough to create a major catastrophe in a densely populated city. As it was, roads, bridges, and buildings over a wide area were extensively damaged by the quake and its many aftershocks.

Subsequent field investigations found no evidence that the White Creek Fault had ruptured in the previous 18,000 years. Older river terraces are displaced by more than the 1929 movement, so there have been repeated offsets, but the intervals may be tens of thousands of years. White Creek is the most easterly of five roughly parallel faults between Murchison and Westport (figure 20; plates 52, 53 and 56). A new underground fault (the jury is still out on whether it is newly developed or just newly discovered) ruptured near Inangahua in 1968, causing the largest onshore earthquake since the 1931 quake at Napier. Inangahua and Murchison share the same seismic neighbourhood (figures 8 and 10).

The shallow 1968 Inangahua quake, also centred in a sparsely populated area, resulted in three deaths and fourteen injuries. Aftershocks, some 800 within the first six weeks, continued for more than three years (plates 54 and 55). The mainshock had a magnitude of 7.1, and surface deformation included numerous short ruptures, up to nearly 3 metres of local uplift, and hundreds of landslides. In spite of comprehensive geological, seismological, and geophysical studies, many believe the debate is incomplete regarding the main displace-

Figure 20 Faults in the Nelson area. New Zealand's oldest rocks and fossils are found here, and the area's long history is evidenced by its numerous fault scars. They range from the now inactive Anatoki Fault that separates a 400- to 500-million-year-old terrane from a younger one, to the still active faults of the Waimea-Flaxmore Fault Zone. 'Terranes' are like plates from an ancient tectonic regime.

The Nelson region has had seventeen quakes greater than magnitude 6 since European settlement and can expect to be shaken at MM-VII intensity about once every 50 years.

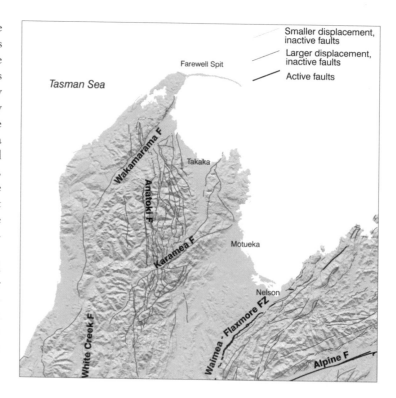

ment mechanism that caused the earthquake. However, both the Inangahua and Murchison earthquakes are typical results of tectonic forces compressing the crust and causing ruptures along reverse faults. This contrasts with the Alpine and Marlborough faults where the movement is dominantly strike-slip to the right, and the reverse movement is secondary.

Otago–Southland

The main signs of earth deformation in the southernmost tectonic province are faults on the eastern flank of the Southern Alps and in Central Otago. The range and basin landforms of Central Otago developed through the growth of steeply dipping reverse faults during the last 2 million years, or thereabouts. Many of these faults developed (or became active) as normal faults more than 100 million years ago. However, they were reactivated as reverse faults because of the convergence of the Australian and Pacific plates, and their proximity to the plate boundary. Much of Otago's continuing regional uplift and deformation is accommodated by 10-km-scale folds and buckles within the widespread flat-lying schist.

Many Central Otago faults are about 50 km long and their average rates of movement, calculated from field observations, are less than 1 mm per year.

Field geology and some computer models suggest that quiet and active periods may alternate, and each last for thousands to tens of thousands of years. The Pisa, Lindis, Dunstan and Ranfurly faults in Central Otago are roughly parallel, and all have significant fault traces that have been active in the last 500,000 years (plates 58, 65 and 70). The Ostler Fault, in the Mackenzie Basin near Lake Ohau, has a 100-m high fault scarp and is more than 50 km long. It is a thrust fault, and a zone of multiple surface ruptures tells of repeated fault displacement. It was last active 3500 years ago and it may move in 2-metre jumps (plates 57, 59 and 60).

No significant historical earthquakes have occurred, which is somewhat surprising. The area is currently seismically quiet and there are no ways of determining when it might jolt into action. Scientists have predicted that future earthquakes causing surface ruptures are likely to be greater than magnitude 7 and involve up to 50 km of surface rupture.

There are numerous visible faults within 100 km of Dunedin (plates 64, 66, 67 and 70), but many of them had their most glorious moments during a time of tectonic extension some 90 to 130 million years ago. After sleeping for more than 100 million years, they reactivated about 15 million years ago. At that time, some faulting became associated with the volcanism near the coast. The Dunedin group of volcanoes straddles the Akatore, Titri, and North Taieri faults, and many small intrusions of igneous rock occurred along, or beside, other faults (plates 68 and 69).

Fault scarps, deformed gravel beds and raised marine terraces indicate intermittent movement on the Akatore and Titri faults throughout the last 2 million years, and the greatest local hazard to Dunedin comes from the still active Akatore Fault. The 1974 Dunedin earthquake was the strongest since the city was founded. This magnitude 4.9 quake probably originated 12 km down on the Akatore Fault, a reverse fault with an onshore trace from the Taieri to the Tokomairiro river mouths. Minor damage, such as cracked or toppled chimneys, was widespread and consistent in suburbs on low-lying soft sediments.

The southernmost coastal region has numerous major fault traces that have had various histories since about 50 million years ago, but few have been active in the last 2 million years. Western Otago and Southland are much more likely to be shaken up by seismic activity in the Fiordland area because of the close proximity of the plate boundary than by quakes on a local fault (plates 61, 62 and 63). Both the Otago and the Nelson–Westland provinces have similar long-term earthquake activity (known from fieldwork) that is at variance with their historical records. Otago's history is much quieter than expected, while Nelson–Westland has had more activity than expected from geological analyses.

Canterbury–Chathams

Few active faults are known in this tectonic province and the area competes with Northland for the prize for the quietest province. However, although the Canterbury–Chathams area is tectonically stable in itself, there is a mighty big but. Scientists estimate that ruptures and earthquakes in the neighbouring Axial Tectonic Belt are likely to cause significant property damage, and possibly loss of life, in Christchurch every 55 years on average. Christchurch suffers moderate to severe ground shaking whenever rocks rupture on faults next door, and the city is a mere 125 km from the Alpine Fault.

Parts of the Canterbury–Chathams province, particularly areas with a high water table and saturated sand, silt and peat near the surface, could be susceptible to liquefaction when severe or prolonged seismic shaking occurs. The only reported instance, however, is from Kaiapoi in 1901 after an earthquake estimated at magnitude 7 occurred near Cheviot.

A magnitude 5.7 earthquake in 1869, called New Brighton after what is now a suburb of Christchurch, is possibly the only local quake since historical records began — certainly no epicentres have been recorded within this tectonic province since 1946. Most of the onshore area is covered by very young sediments washed out by glaciers and rivers, and these may hide evidence of fault traces and movements.

The active Ashley Fault, 20 km north of Christchurch, is at the northern edge of the province and it is the eastern part of the Porters Pass–Amberley Fault Zone. The Ashley Fault has a 3-km-long fault scarp on the north bank of the Ashley River, but little is yet known about its history of movement.

The quiet province

The Western North Island tectonic province is relatively stable with only a few active faults, and its fault movements average less than 1 mm per year. The area west of Wanganui hosted two quakes of about magnitude 7 during the nineteenth century, but neither they, nor any since, are known to have ruptured the surface. Several fault traces are visible in the Nukumaru and Waverley fault zones, which are active, but they do not seem to be associated with the numerous shallow earthquakes that occur offshore in the Wanganui Basin.

A band of smallish shallow earthquakes runs from Ruapehu to Mt Taranaki (map 2), but most of Taranaki's earthquakes are much deeper and originate from the subducting Pacific Plate, not from deformation within the overlying Australian crust.

The Inglewood Fault between Mt Taranaki and New Plymouth is the only significant active fault with a surface rupture in this province apart from the

Kerepehi Fault, which runs north–south down the Hauraki Plains. The tectonic map of New Zealand for the last 500,000 years (published in 1983) shows absolutely no active faults with surface ruptures north of the plains. The Wairoa North fault near Clevedon is now known to be active, and while there may be some others, they are considered either insignificant or probably inactive (plate 30).

The seismic risk of a region is calculated as the region's 'hazard' multiplied by its 'vulnerability'. Auckland does not need to put earthquakes near the top of its list of natural hazards and environmental challenges, but it has a moderate seismic risk. Compared to the rest of the country its hazard is low, but the sheer size of the place gives it a high vulnerability factor. The size of earthquakes that Wellingtonians readily withstand every six years or so is estimated to shake Auckland just once every 62 years, and the residents of Whangarei once every 220 to 330 years. Local earthquakes that do affect the wider Auckland region mostly originate in the crust under the Hunua Ranges and are smaller than magnitude 5.

There is sporadic, low-magnitude seismicity throughout Waikato and Coromandel, much of it associated with extensional movements under the Hauraki Plains. The Kerepihi Fault is considered active, but with recurrence intervals of magnitude 7 earthquakes every 4000 to 8000 years. One segment has ruptured within the last 1800 years, because volcanic debris from the great Taupo Eruption has been displaced. The magnitude 5.3 Te Aroha earthquake in 1972 was probably associated with movement on the Hauraki Fault, but no surface ruptures were reported. It was felt as intensity MMVII in Te Aroha and created a substantial amount of minor damage.

The shallow Waikato Heads earthquake in 1891, estimated to be smaller than magnitude 6, remains the most intense historical quake that the region has produced. It was reported at intensity MMVI from Kawhia Harbour to Auckland, but damage was minimal. Earthquakes centred elsewhere in New Zealand are likely to wobble Auckland more than homegrown efforts.

Farther north qualifies as the least seismically active area in the country. Four earthquakes have been recorded in the Kaitaia area since 1840, but none had a magnitude greater than 3.9. Although earthquakes located elsewhere in New Zealand are occasionally felt in northern Northland, shaking intensities greater than MMV are not expected in the future.

HELPFUL HARDWARE

To record the movement of the ground during an earthquake, a stationary point to work from is needed. The method that seismologists adopt makes use of inertia; the tendency that a heavy body has to stay put, particularly if it is not attached firmly to the ground. A weight hanging from a flexible support tends to lag behind when the support is moved. If the support is firmly fixed to the ground, and some method of recording the relative movement of the weight and the support is provided, we have a primitive form of seismograph.

A seismograph comprises a seismometer, which senses the ground motion, and a recorder that creates a visual record of the motion. Inside the seismometer, there is a 1-kg mass with a pickup coil wound around it. The mass is attached to a spring, and moves between the poles of a magnet mounted to the case. As it does so, an electric current is generated in the pickup coil, with the size of the current depending on the speed at which the coil travels. This electric current is fed into an amplifier in the recorder, and then on to a pen-motor that makes a visual record of the ground motion on paper fixed to a rotating drum.

Seismographs have a clock that feeds minute-marks and hour-marks to the pen-motor. This clock can be calibrated with broadcast time signals (radio pips) so that a common time base is established between seismographs. Synchronisation is essential for accurately locating where earthquakes originate, and their epicentres.

Modern seismographs are directly linked to computers so the pen, paper, and rotating drum combinations are replaced by records on disk that are displayed on computer screens. For those who like to stand and stare, these continuously fill up with wiggly lines ... At sites on hard rock, well away from staircases, traffic and other sources of artificial ground noise, the ground motion can be magnified over a million times by a seismograph. This means that even extremely small earthquakes can be picked up and recorded.

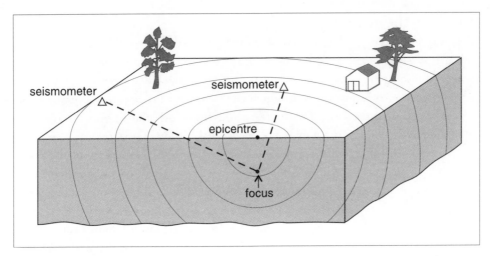

Figure 21 Plotting the directions from which waves reach at least two recording stations roughly locates the epicentre, the point on the surface that is vertically above the focus.

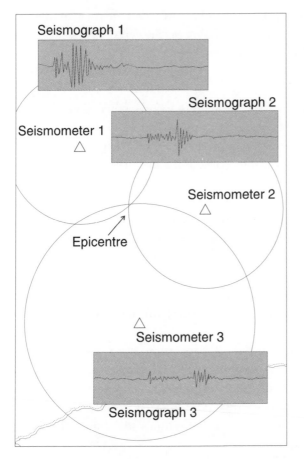

Figure 22 Sophisticated models for pinpointing the epicentre of a quake come from straightforward geometry and physics. At least three seismographs are needed, but it is definitely a case of the more the merrier.

The maximum distance that the epicentre could be from each seismograph is calculated and circles are drawn with that distance as the radius. The circles intersect at the epicentre. For distances up to 1000 km from the focus, the average P-wave speed varies between 5 and 9 km per second depending on the rock types it passes through. The slower S-wave averages between 3 and 5 km/s and it is also affected by the density of the rocks in its path. Furthermore, S-waves do not travel through water or liquid rock, such as magma.

Finding the focus

Seismographs record the passage of waves generated by earthquakes. By making a few simple measurements of these waves, the point within the earth where the fault began to break — its focus — is located. These calculations depend on the different rates at which the two main types of earthquake wave travel through the earth. The fastest, and therefore the first to arrive anywhere, is the P-wave. The S-wave is considerably slower.

Because the speed of seismic waves increases with the density of the material that they travel through, the speed of waves in the earth is much faster than in air. As the waves travel greater distances from their source, they penetrate deeper into the earth, and their average speed increases with increasing distance. Such variations require sophisticated and complex mathematical calculations. To locate the focus, the times that the P- and S-waves arrive at each seismograph are measured, and a guess is made about where the quake originated (figure 21). This need not be a very good guess — the seismograph with the earliest arrival times is usually taken as a good starting point (this initial guess is politely termed a 'first approximation'). Using mathematical models of the way that seismic-wave speeds vary depending on the type of rock that they travel through, the times at which the seismic waves would arrive at the stations from the guessed focus are calculated. These times are then compared with the real arrival times.

The difference between the observed and predicted arrival times is then used to make a better estimate of the focus of the earthquake. From this second guess, another set of arrival times is predicted, and another comparison with the real times is measured. Further corrections are made, which lead to further predictions, and so on.

This process continues until no further improvements can be made in matching the real arrival times with those that are theoretically calculated. The final estimate is deemed the focus. All this repetition is not quite as tedious as it sounds, because the whole business can be done in a matter of seconds with computer assistance.

Most measurements involve some errors, and our understanding of the speeds and pathways that earthquake waves travel through the earth is not complete. This is mainly because different geological strata, structures, and rock types have different densities and their distribution deep underground is not precisely known. Seismologists working with data from New Zealand's nationwide seismograph network use four different velocity/depth models to calculate travel times of waves passing through the crust in different parts of the country. Even so, the final focus fix probably does not match the exact point at which the earthquake began.

Figure 23 Seismograms from five seismographs at varying distances from the focus of an earthquake.

The interval between the arrival time of the P-wave and the slower S-wave increases with increasing distance from the focus. Note also how the amplitude (the size of the wiggles) becomes smaller the farther a seismograph is from the focus of an earthquake.

People in the neighbourhood of the last seismograph (250 km from the focus) would not have felt the earthquake at all.

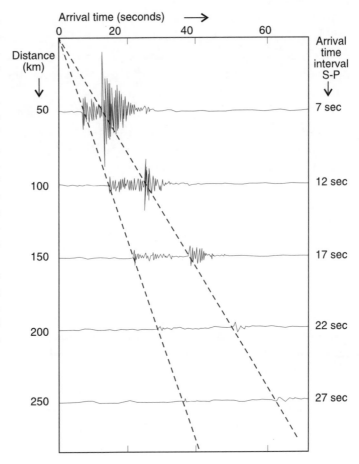

Statistical theory helps us estimate the size of the discrepancy based on the closeness of the final match between real and calculated arrival times. For earthquakes that have been clearly recorded on the Wellington seismograph network, the average error is about 1 km. If this sounds like a lot, remember that an 'average' P-wave left the focus at about 8 km per second, so it took only one-eighth of a second to travel the possibly erroneous kilometre. Furthermore, the accuracy with which the arrivals can be timed is usually only about one-tenth of a second. Thus, a one-kilometre uncertainty is close to the best that current technology can achieve.

Occur, recur, recurrent?

How often and when? How long is a piece of string? Unfortunately, there is no sensible and practical answer to questions regarding the timing of earthquakes, and destructive earthquakes will continue to catch communities unaware. However, two general points are useful and scientifically acceptable. Firstly, quakes occur more frequently the closer an area is to a plate boundary. Secondly, the mean return period of large quakes and their size can be calculated for various areas if enough geological and seismological research has been done. That is, when the average number of years expected to pass between earthquakes, of a particular intensity in a particular place, is known.

Earthquakes are unstoppable, but their dangers and disasters can be minimised by combining good science with regional and local planning decisions. Knowing how often damaging quakes recur is crucial for planning authority rulings, civil defence plans, and drawing up building codes that are designed to protect people and property from earthquake damage. Under the Resource Management Act passed in 1991, local and regional politicians and planners are legally responsible for reducing the vulnerability of their communities to natural hazards.

Although some areas are much more quake-prone than others, nearly all regions follow a pattern regarding recurrence rates and magnitudes. The rule-of-thumb is that recurrence rates increase ten times with every drop of magnitude unit. So, the region that has one M8+ every 500 years can anticipate ten M7s, 100 M6s, 1000 M5s and so on, over the same period. On a global scale, the annual frequency-magnitude relationship is:

> one quake at M>8
> 13 at M>7
> 108 at M>6
> 800 at M>5
> 6200 at M>4

Millions of lives and billions of dollars worth of property depend on geoscience and engineering research to lower the risk from geological hazards. Recurrence rates are calculated using statistical analyses of repeat times for past quakes of a particular magnitude within a given region.

Hazards and risks

Earthquake hazards potentially pose a serious threat to many parts of New Zealand because of the country's location astride the boundary between the Pacific and Australian tectonic plates. Earthquake hazards include ground shaking, ground rupture, liquefaction, landslides and tsunami, as well as secondary problems such as fire, and damaged buildings, roads and bridges.

Hazards vary around New Zealand, not only because of the magnitude, location, and depth of an earthquake, but also because of the geological materials that underlie a particular place. Technically, seismic hazard is the probability of a damaging ground movement over a given period at a given site. Because New Zealand is so geologically active, it is inevitable that a destructive quake will eventually strike a major population centre.

New Zealand geoscientists operate more than 300 accelerographs and acceleroscopes to monitor strong shaking in towns and cities, and on dams and bridges. The nationwide seismograph network includes 33 digital stations, four analogue stations, and seven regional networks. About half are connected to a continuously recording computer system. Temporary networks are moved around as necessary to monitor special activity, particularly aftershock patterns.

Earthquake risk is the product of natural hazard and vulnerability. This risk is the degree of damage and loss in terms of lives and dollars expected in a community for a given sized quake. It is expressed as a fraction or percentage of the total exposure for a given event. Therefore, risk increases as population increases; for instance, there is a much greater earthquake risk in Wellington than Inangahua.

As it is impossible to reduce earthquake risk by modifying the size and location of the hazard, geoscientists, engineers, and planners collaborate to reduce vulnerability and assess the hazard. Appropriate building codes are essential, and zoning for certain types of buildings and land usage helps. Roads, bridges, and water and electrical services are among the community developments that can be modified. In this way, their vulnerability can be reduced.

New Zealand building codes, for example, only have to take into account ground accelerations at half the levels that were actually measured at Kobe, Japan in 1995 and Northridge, California in 1993. These codes are adequate except near big faults, such as the Wellington Fault, where buildings are designed to higher requirements. In some parts of the world, insurance and financial companies play a role in influencing citizens away from hazard zones, such as Hawaii's lava paths, by making it harder to finance and insure buildings in those areas.

All these strategies to reduce seismic risk, however, depend on a solid understanding of the occurrence and effects of earthquakes. The best protection against earthquake damage from a national viewpoint is good geological and geophysical science. It is only when scientists understand the processes and hazards in a given area that they can present information and arguments to help politicians and planners make the legal and economic decisions necessary to protect communities from the worst effects of hazards.

Table 3 Mean return periods in years for particular earthquake shaking intensities at various New Zealand locations. Geoscientists are constantly revising and refining this chart — just stay prepared.

Area	MMVI	MMVII	MMVIII	MMIX
Kaitaia	300	1200		
Whangarei	130	630		
Auckland	57	240	1300	
Tauranga	5	21	89	420
Hamilton	19	75	340	2200
Whakatane	4	24	99	400
Rotorua	5	23	97	460
Gisborne	10	62	200	560
Taupo	5	42	190	1100
New Plymouth	13	51	200	920
Napier/Hastings	11	62	210	640
Wanganui	5	25	120	540
Palmerston North	8	35	130	440
Masterton	12	41	130	410
Wellington/Hutt Valley	8	32	100	370
Nelson	6	25	88	340
Blenheim	7	26	92	360
Westport	12	40	140	580
Kaikoura	9	31	110	410
Greymouth	14	47	170	680
Christchurch	21	70	2507	980
Mt Cook	19	66	240	930
Timaru	36	130	470	2400
Milford Sound	28	150	750	
Queenstown	24	100	430	2000
Oamaru	41	150	580	
Dunedin	51	200	820	650
Invercargill	31	120	460	2400

Scientists monitor ground movements, pinpoint areas sensitive to hazards, assess the probability of damaging quakes occurring, and estimate the severity of their effects in order to develop strategies for minimising earthquake risk.

The Resource Management Act requires local and regional authorities to protect the public and the environment from natural hazards. This is forcing decision-makers to learn about the nature, location, and effects of earthquake hazards, and to develop policies to monitor and limit their downside. The more geoscience research that is available, the better the policies and standards to protect New Zealanders from quake damage will be.

Earthquake prediction for beginners

Can we give warning of earthquakes in New Zealand?

If you mean can geoscientists say that there will be an earthquake on some particular day, the answer is 'no'.

So, what is known about future earthquakes?

a) Geoscientists can tell how often, on average, you can expect to be shaken by an earthquake, and how strongly, in your part of New Zealand.

b) Geoscientists can tell which parts of New Zealand are most at risk and which are safest from quakes.

c) Geoscientists can tell roughly how much shaking an earthquake of a particular magnitude (or strength) will produce.

d) Geoscientists can recognise, and warn people about, hazards that will be especially dangerous in an earthquake, such as:

- fault-related risks to buildings — splitting in two, or having foundations cracked by ground-level changes, as well as general damage,
- slope risks such as landslides and slumps,
- water risks — tsunami, and pipe and dam breakages,
- liquefaction.

Will geoscientists ever be able to give 'real' warnings?

Maybe.

How will they try?

There are three major areas of research for earthquake prediction. These are foreshocks and seismic cycles, fault history, and earth-deformation and geophysical monitoring.

Foreshocks can sometimes give a warning. The trouble with them is that an earthquake cannot be called a foreshock until a larger earthquake follows it closely in time. It just looks like an ordinary earthquake, so until geoscientists can find better ways of distinguishing them from other small earthquakes (so far they cannot), they are unreliable.

Establishing seismic cycles of foreshock, main quake, and aftershock sequences requires more information (from all round the world) than is currently available. Global patterns are even more complicated because it is certain that patterns of frequency change with time and differ in different areas. For example, two neighbouring regions in Turkey alternate in 500-year cycles for seismic activity. Another complication is that some earthquakes occur in swarms with many shocks closely grouped in time and space, but with no single outstanding event.

Fault histories help because big earthquakes usually happen on big and existing faults. Many geologists consider that most big faults 'specialise' in a characteristic size of earthquake that occurs every few hundred to a few thousand years. So, if you can discover the dates of previous quakes on a big fault, you can estimate when the next is due to within tens to hundreds of years. Geologists have ways of dating past fault movements, such as radiostope dating, but nearly all methods currently used have quite large margins of error.

There are two basic approaches to using fault histories for predicting earthquakes. One focuses on where quakes have occurred in the past, and presumes that history repeats itself. Virtually all geological research over the last century indicates that this 'history repeats itself' assumption is solid. The other targets segments of a seismic belt that have not had recent quakes and assumes that the gap is overdue for movement. Statisticians do not consider that seismic gaps are reliable indicators of future activity, but geologists generally feel that the longer it is from the last quake, the closer it is to the next.

Before some earth-quaking ruptures there have been slow ground movements, measured by advanced geodetic surveying techniques. Measurable changes to other properties can also herald a build-up of earth deformation that may result in rock rupture and an earthquake. For example, changes in the temperature of water in deep wells, the levels of water in wells, fluctuations in the water table (that are independent of climate), and the resistance of the ground to electric currents are good indicators. Shortly before some earthquakes in other parts of the world, there have been sudden jumps in the rate at which these changes were happening — sometimes only hours before a big quake. The value of comprehensive and continuous monitoring can not be overestimated.

Therefore, if New Zealand geoscientists have the right instruments in the right places, and learn to recognise the symptoms, the day may eventually come when they really can say, 'We will have an earthquake tomorrow.' And be right!

Table 4 Vital statistics of some of New Zealand's more notable earthquakes. Earthquake time is given in the 24-hour clock of Universal Time, the modern replacement of Greenwich Mean Time.

Earthquake	Date	Magnitude	Depth	Intensity	Fault type
Wairarapa	23 Jan 1855	~8.0-8.2	shallow	MMX	Strike-slip, some reverse slip
Glynn Wye, Nth Canterbury	31 Aug 1888	~7.0-7.3	<12 km	MMIX	Strike-slip
Bay of Plenty	22 Nov 1914	>7.2	300 km	MMVIII	Subduction
Arthur's Pass	9 Mar 1929	7.1	11 km	MMVIII	Strike-slip
Buller (Murchison)	16 June 1929	7.8	9 km	MMIX	Reverse
Napier (Hawke's Bay)	3 Feb 1931	7.8	15 km	MMX	Strike-slip, some reverse slip
Napier aftershock	13 Feb 1931	7.3	16 km	MMVII	Mainly strike-slip
Wairoa	15 Sept 1932	6.9	8 km	MMIX	Strike-slip
Pahiatua	5 Mar 1934	7.6	~30 km	MMVII	Strike-slip
Wairarapa	24 June 1942	7.2	12 km	MMVIII	Strike-slip
Bay of Plenty	29 Sept 1953	7.2	273 km	MMVI	Subduction
Inangahua	23 May 1968	7.1	10 km	MMX	Reverse
Taumarunui (North Island)	5 Jan 1973	6.6	149 km	MMVI	Subduction
Edgecumbe	2 Mar 1987	6.1	6 km	MMIX	Normal
Macquarie Ridge	23 May 1989	8.2	10 km		Strike-slip
Weber	19 Feb 1990	6.2	23 km	MMVII	Normal, some strike-slip
Fiordland (offshore)	10 Aug 1993	7.0	25 km		Reverse
Arthur's Pass	18 June 1994	6.7	5 km	MMVII	Reverse
East Cape (offshore)	6 Feb 1995	7.1	~12 km		Normal

GLOSSARY

Accelerogram   the printed or digital record of an accelerograph.

Accelerograph   a type of seismograph designed to measure ground acceleration at the surface.

Aftershocks   earthquakes, usually smaller than the mainshock, that follow a large shallow earthquake, originate in the same area, and occur at a higher rate than the regional background rate.

Amplitude   the maximum height of a wave crest. Modern seismographs can detect waves with amplitudes of only a few nanometres (millionths of a millimetre).

Characteristic earthquake   the typical earthquake expected to result from repeated displacement on a given fault segment.

Compressional stress   a force that shortens.

Convection   a mechanism of heat transfer that moves material. Hot material rises because of its lesser density, and cold material sinks.

Core   the central part of the Earth, below the mantle at a depth of about 2900 km. It is liquid — we know that because S-waves will not travel through it. There is also an inner core, which is solid.

Crust   this is the name given to the top concentric layer of the Earth. Its thickness averages about 40 km under most continents and about 6 km under oceans.

Crustal earthquakes   generally less than 15 km deep, particularly those occurring in continental crust overlying a subduction zone.

Deep-sea trench   a long and deep undersea valley that is the boundary between the two colliding plates where one plate descends beneath the other.

Deep-slab earthquakes   produced by extension stresses within a subducting plate.

Deformation   a general term for processes of folding, faulting, and shearing in rocks as a result of various tectonic forces. Also used synonymously for strain: change in the shape or volume of a rock mass because of the stresses acting upon it.

Dip   the maximum angle between an inclined plane and a horizontal plane.

Ductile   capable of undergoing changes in shape without breaking.

Earthquake   a shaking movement of the ground caused by seismic waves radiating from the rupture of rock underground.

Elastic rebound   the energy that deforms the earth is stored rather like a rubber band being stretched. Eventually the strength of the rocks is overcome and rupture occurs. The deformed material on each side of the rupture 'rebounds' to near its original shape, but is displaced from the material on the opposite side.

Epicentral distance   the distance from the epicentre to the place in question.

Epicentre   the point on the earth's surface directly above the place where the earthquake originated.

Fault   a fracture or fracture zone in a rock mass across which there has been displacement of one side relative to the other.

Fault plane   the areal surface of the rupture that offsets rocks and creates a geological fault.

Fault scarp   a slope or long bank formed by displacement of rocks on either side of a fault.

Fault trace   the intersection of a fault plane with the surface of the earth. This may be visible as a sudden change in topography.

Focus   the underground place where the earth-quaking rupture began. It is given a latitude, longitude, and depth. It is mapped as the point where the earthquake originated.

Footwall   rock on the underlying side of a sloping (dipping) fault plane.

Frequency   the number of wave peaks, or troughs, passing a given point within a specified time. From small earthquakes nearby, the frequency could be many times per second. Large surface waves from distant earthquakes have a frequency of only two or three times per minute (*see* period).

Hanging wall   rock on the overlying side of a sloping (dipping) fault plane.

Ignimbrite   volcanic rock created by flows of ash, pumice and gas after explosive eruptions.

Intensity   a measure of how strong the shaking is at any particular place during an earthquake. It is usually measured on the descriptive Modified Mercalli Intensity Scale, which has twelve levels.

Isoseismal   contour lines on a map separating different levels of seismic intensity.

Liquefaction   the rearrangement of particles in water-saturated material because of earthquake shaking, so that the mixture acts as a fluid, rather than a solid.

Lithosphere   the outer 100 km of the earth that, along with its crust, makes up tectonic plates.

Magnitude   different types of magnitude scale exist to measure the size of an earthquake at its focus. Magnitude does not measure how badly you are shaken, but the amount of energy released. An increase of one whole unit in magnitude is equivalent to an increase of more than 30 in the energy released.

Mantle   the layer of the earth comprising most of the planet's interior. It lies between the crust and the core. It is mostly solid, so P-waves and S-waves can travel through it.

Normal fault   a fault in which the hanging wall has moved downward relative to the footwall because of extensional stress.

Oceanic ridge   a major and continuous elevated range on the sea floor that is the boundary between two plates that are being created and moving apart.

P-wave   the primary and fastest type of wave radiating out from a seismic focus. Like sound waves, the actual movement of the solid medium is in the same direction as the wave is travelling.

Paleoseismology   the investigation of prehistoric earthquakes and their effects.

Period   the time between successive cycles of a seismic wave; the reciprocal of the frequency.

Plate   a large rigid section of the earth's outer mantle, plus the crust, that moves in relation to other plates and the interior of the earth.

Prediction   a forecast that an event will occur. This branch of seismology is not yet well advanced, but research is being done in many countries.

Range and basin topography   alternating ranges and valleys created by a series of tilted blocks with at least one side bounded by (reverse) faults, such as are found in Central Otago.

Reverse fault   a fault in which the hanging wall moves upwards relative to the footwall, because of compressional stress.

Rock   a solid cohesive aggregate of one or more minerals.

S-wave   the secondary seismic wave, which travels more slowly than the P-wave. The vibration of the solid medium is at right angles to the direction of travel, like a wave on a rope where the rope actually moves sideways as the wave passes along. S-waves cannot travel through liquids.

Sand boil   a sand deposit formed by the expulsion of liquefied sand from subsurface sources because of ground shaking during an earthquake.

Seismic velocity   the speed at which seismic waves travel within the earth. P-waves travel the fastest, followed by S-waves, and then surface waves.

Seismicity   the distribution of earthquakes both geographically and through time.

Seismogram   the record made by a seismograph.

Seismograph   an instrument that registers earthquakes. It consists of a seismometer and a recording device.

Seismology   literally 'the study of things that shake'. The study of earthquakes and the use of earthquakes to study the interior structure of the earth.

Seismometer   an instrument that detects earthquake pulses, and movements of the ground.

Shear   deformation resulting from stresses that cause touching points to move apart in a direction parallel to their plane of contact.

Strain   change in the shape or volume of a rock mass because of stresses acting upon it.

Stratigraphy   the study of rock strata, particularly the description and interpretation of sedimentary layers.

Strike   the compass direction of a surface, such as a fault plane or sedimentary layer, as it intersects the horizontal. Strike is a horizontal measure.

Strike-slip fault   a fault along which movement parallels the strike of the fault, that is, the displacement is horizontal.

Subduction   the process of one lithospheric plate descending beneath another.

Subduction-thrust earthquake   a (usually) enormous plate-boundary earthquake created by a rupture on the interface between a subducting and overlying plate.

Subduction zone   a long narrow region along which subduction takes place.

Surface wave   surface waves spread away from the epicentre over the surface of the earth. They travel slowly and mostly have long periods.

Tephra   a general term for all types of volcanic material that is deposited by falling through the air.

Zoning   the identification of various regions in which earthquakes are more likely, and where structures are required to be built more strongly.

REFERENCES

Aitken, J.J.amd Lowry, M.A., 1995. More earthquakes explained. *Institute of Geological & Nuclear Sciences information series* 35.

Aitken, J.J., 1996. Plate tectonics for curious kiwis. *Institute of Geological & Nuclear Sciences information series* 42.

Allaby, A. and Allaby, M., (eds), 1992. *The Concise Oxford Dictionary of Earth Sciences.* Oxford: Oxford University Press.

Anderson, H.J., *et al.*, 1994. The 1968 May 23 Inangahua, New Zealand, earthquake: an integrated geological, geodetic, and seismological source model. *New Zealand journal of geology and geophysics* 37:59–86.

Anderson, H.J.and Webb, T., 1994. New Zealand seismicity: patterns revealed by the upgraded National Seismograph Network. *New Zealand journal of geology and geophysics* 37:477–493.

Bates, R.L.and Jackson, J.A., 1987. *Glossary of geology.* Virginia: American Geological Institute. Third Edition.

Beanland, S. and Haines, J., 1998. The kinematics of active deformation in the North Island, New Zealand, determined from geological strain rates. *New Zealand journal of geology and geophysics* 41:311–323.

Beanland, S., *et al.*, 1998. Structure and deformational history of the inner forearc region, Hikurangi subduction margin, New Zealand. *New Zealand journal of geology and geophysics* 41:325–342.

Begg, J.G. and Van Dissen, R.J., 1998. Whitemans Valley Fault: a newly discovered active second order fault near Wellington, New Zealand implications for regional seismic hazard. *New Zealand journal of geology and geophysics* 41:441–448.

Berryman, K.R., 1993. Age, height, and deformation of Holocene marine terraces at Mahia Peninsula, Hikurangi subduction margin, New Zealand. *Tectonics* 12:1347–1364.

Berryman, K.R. and Beanland, S., 1988. Ongoing deformation of New Zealand: rates of tectonic movement from geological evidence. *Transactions of the Institution of Professional Engineers New Zealand* 15:25–35.

Bishop, D.G., 1994. Geology of the Milton area 1:50 000. *Institute of Geological & Nuclear Sciences geological map* 9.

Bolt, B.A., 1988. *Earthquakes: a primer.* San Fransisco: W.H. Freeman.

Brown, L.J. and Weeber, J.H., 1992. Geology of the Christchurch urban area 1:25 000. *Institute of Geological & Nuclear Sciences geological map* 1.

Challis, G.A., *et al.*, 1994. Geology of the Lake Rotoroa area, Nelson. *Institute of Geological & Nuclear Sciences geological map* 8.

Cooper, A.F. and Norris, R.J., 1995. Displacement on the Alpine Fault at Haast River, South Westland, New Zealand. *New Zealand journal of geology and geophysics* 38:509–514.

Cowan, H., 1994. *Field guide to New Zealand active tectonics: IASPEI 94.* Wellington: SIR Publishing.

Cox, S.C. and Findlay, R.H., 1995. The Main Divide Fault Zone and its role in the formation of the Southern Alps, New Zealand. *New Zealand journal of geology and geophysics* 38:489–500.

Downes, G.L., 1995. The atlas of isoseismal maps of New Zealand earthquakes. *Institute of Geological & Nuclear Sciences monograph* 11.

Dowrick, D.J., 1994. Damage and intensities in the magnitude 7.8 1929 Murchison, New Zealand, earthquake. *Bulletin of the New Zealand National Society for Earthquake Engineering* 27:190–203.

Eiby, G.A., 1989. *Earthquakes*. Auckland: HeinemannReed.

Grapes, R., *et al.*, 1998. Rupturing of the Awatere Fault during the 1848 October 16 Marlborough earthquake, New Zealand: historical and present day evidence. *New Zealand journal of geology and geophysics* 41:387–399.

Isaac, M.J., 1996. Geology of the Kaitaia area 1:250 000. *Institute of Geological & Nuclear Sciences geological map* 1.

Johnston, M.R., 1996. Geology of the D'Urville area 1:50 000. *Institute of Geological & Nuclear Sciences geological map* 16.

Johnston, M.R., 1994. Geology of the Richmond Range 1:50 000. *Institute of Geological & Nuclear Sciences geological map* 12.

Kermode, L., 1992. Geology of the Auckland urban area 1:50 000. *Institute of Geological & Nuclear Sciences geological map* 2.

Lay, T. and Wallace, T.C., 1995. *Modern global seismology*. San Diego: Academic Press.

Massey, W., *et al.*, 1992. *Architectural design for earthquakes*. Auckland: New Zealand National Society for Earthquake Engineering.

McCalpin, J.P., (ed.), 1998. *Paleoseismology*. San Diego: Academic Press.

Officers of the New Zealand Geological Survey, 1983. Late Quaternary tectonic map of New Zealand. *Institute of Geological & Nuclear Sciences miscellaneous map* 12.

Reyners, M., 1998. Plate coupling and the hazard of large subduction thrust earthquakes at the Hikurangi subduction zone, New Zealand. *New Zealand journal of geology and geophysics* 41:343–354.

Reyners, M., *et al.*, 1998. The Ormond, New Zealand, earthquake of 1993 August 10: rupture in the mantle of the subducted Pacific Plate. *New Zealand journal of geology and geophysics* 41:179–186.

Ruscoe, Q., 1988. *Walking on jelly: the Bay of Plenty earthquake 1987*. DSIR information series 164.

Smith, W.D. and Berryman, K.R., 1983. Revised estimates of earthquake hazard in New Zealand. *Bulletin of the New Zealand National Society for Earthquake Engineering* 16:259–272.

Smith, I.E.M., (ed.), 1986. Late Cenozoic volcanism in New Zealand. *The Royal Society of New Zealand Bulletin* 23.

Stevens, G.R., 1990. Rugged Landscape: the geology of central New Zealand, including Wellington, Wairarapa, Manawatu and the Marlborough Sounds. *DSIR information series* 169.

Stirling, M.W., *et al.*, 1998. Probabilistic seismic hazard analysis of New Zealand. *New Zealand journal of geology and geophysics* 41:355–375.

Suggate, R.P., 1994. Comment and reply on The 1968 May 23 Inangahua, New Zealand, earthquake: an integrated geological, geodetic and seismological source model. *New Zealand journal of geology and geophysics* 37:498–501.

Watt, F., 1993. *Usborne understanding geography: earthquakes and volcanoes*. London: Usborne Publishing.

Yang, J.S., 1992. Landslide mapping and major earthquakes on the Kakapo Fault, South Island, New Zealand. *Journal of the Royal Society of New Zealand* 22:205–212.

Yeats, R.S., *et al.*, 1997. *The geology of earthquakes*. London: Oxford University Press.

Yetton, M.D., 1998. Progress in understanding the paleoseismicity of the central and northern Alpine Fault, Westland, New Zealand. *New Zealand journal of geology and geophysics* 41:475–48.

ACKNOWLEDGEMENTS

Aerial photographs were taken by Lloyd Homer of Landscape Photography, Upper Hutt. Figures have been draughted by Wendy St George and Carolyn Hume, both of the Institute of Geological and Nuclear Sciences.

Many geoscientists from the Institute and the University of Otago have taken an active interest in, and made significant contributions to, this project. Particular thanks are due to the reviewers: Dr Kelvin Berryman, Dr Pat Suggate, Dr Terry Webb and Professor Rick Sibson.

With the generosity of spirit typical among Institute geoscientists, maps and diagrams have been contributed by John Beavan, John Begg, Kelvin Berryman, Jim Cousins, David Dowrick, Colin Mazengarb, Mark Rattenbury, Pilar Villamor and Terry Webb, from their own research.

Many photographs were chosen from the personal collections of Kelvin Berryman, Gaye Downes, Graham Hancox, Simon Nathan, Ian Turnbull and Judith Zachariasen. These scientists also freely provided information for the captions, and discussed associated parts of the text.

Additional information, explanations and encouragement came from Institute scientists Dick Beetham, Des Darby, David Heron, Julie Lee, Stuart Read, Martin Reyners, Russell Robinson, Mark Stirling, Rupert Sutherland and Russ Van Dissen, as well as from Dr Daphne Lee and Professor Chuck Landis at the University of Otago.

ABOUT THE AUTHOR

Jefley Aitken has a multidisciplinary geoscience PhD from the University of Otago. Between her masters and doctoral degrees, she spent twelve years as a journalist, writer, and editor. Dr Aitken has been the science writer/editor for the Institute of Geological and Nuclear Sciences since 1994, and became the Publications Manager in 1995.